I'm making
myself fit,
I'm making
myself strong,
I'm making
myself beautiful,
I'm making
myself shine.

This Training Journal Belongs To:

....

On this day of .... I commit to the 8 daily steps of meditation, gratitude, intentions, eating clean, intensity training, staying hydrated, thinking positive thoughts and gaining self-awareness to create a rocking fit body, mind & spirit.

Signed:

....

Dailygreatness
BE YOUR OWN GURU

Dailygreatness Training Journal: 12 Weeks to a Rocking Fit Body, Mind & Spirit

Lyndelle Palmer-Clarke

You've bought the training journal now join Rocking Fit, our 12 week holistic online training program for women at **www.rockingfit.com** and start your journey to health, wellness and empowerment today.

Use Discount Code RFDGTJ to receive 15% off your yearly membership!

Share your journal images using hashtag #rockingfit on social media or review the Dailygreatness Training Journal on Amazon and go in our monthly draw to win a free copy.

To reorder your Dailygreatness Training Journal and browse all our other journals, online courses and content, visit **www.dailygreatness.co**

Design by Viktoriya Nesheva
Printed in China

Dreaming Room Publishing
Second Edition Dreaming Room 2015

Caution! If used every day, this journal could radically transform, profoundly shape and dynamically alter your destiny while motivating you to....

make healthier choices

become fit, healthy and happy

create awesomely inspired goals

regain your zest for life

build discipline

live a healthy lifestyle

uncover blind spots and find solutions to your challenges

overcome limiting beliefs and negative thought patterns

take action and achieve your dreams

overcome self-sabotage

move from being the victim of your life to the powerful creator of your life

I'm so happy that you have chosen to go on this health & wellness journey, where you will be guided and inspired to transform your entire being - your body, your mind & your spirit. I want to congratulate you for taking the courageous step towards a better, more happy, healthy and vibrant you.

Creating the body of your dreams is like starting out on any new adventure. To succeed in reaching your destination, you need a good plan. It's exciting to think where you will be at the end of this journey because, in just 12 weeks, you can literally transform yourself with focused effort and a willingness to succeed.

But let's be really clear here: this journey isn't a bikini body challenge, and it's not a weight loss program. Although you might achieve both, this is so much more. The Dailygreatness Training Journal is a lifestyle upgrade, a journey to holistic health and a simple tool for creating quantum leaps in how you view your health and wellness - starting from the inside out.

Following the steps in this journal will give you the space to reconnect with and reawaken the true potential of your body, your mind and your spirit and to help you remember what is truly possible. When you upgrade what you believe is possible for you: a whole new world opens up. The Dailygreatness Training Journal is your very own personal trainer for the next 12 weeks and is an amazing tool to document your transformation each day, week and month. It brings together all the elements of a successful training program to give you a foundation for achieving your fitness goals.

As you get leaner, stronger and fitter from your workouts and as you train your mind to think empowering and successful thoughts, you'll naturally feel inspired to make this your new way of life. This journal used alongside our 12-week online training program at www.rockingfit.com is even more powerful.

As women and mums, we often give so much to those around us that we neglect to find time for ourselves. The next 12 weeks will require you to be somewhat selfish and to make choices for your highest good. By making space to reconnect with your essence, you connect to the unlimited energy, vitality, creativity and health that naturally resides within you. When you connect to that essence, you have so much more to give to those around you. So, it's not only an investment in yourself but ultimately this is an investment in the people you love most, and there is nothing selfish about that.

During the next 12 weeks, you're going to need to get uncomfortable because it's in those moments of discomfort that you will have your biggest breakthroughs. The big shifts, the big breakthroughs, will come from your inner decision to make change happen -- all you need to do is commit to showing up for yourself and believe that you are worth it. Now is your time to claim back and reignite that lost vibrancy, enthusiasm and playfulness you once had for life or to simply shine even brighter.

I dedicate this journal to the women who believe they deserve a Rocking Fit® life and who are willing to do what it takes to get there. Now it's just up to you to step up to the challenge.

Wishing you every success,

Lyndelle

The Body-Mind Connection

Creating a Rocking Fit® body, starts with a Rocking Fit® mind. Healthy thinking creates healthy behaviours, and it's our behaviour that determines our results. We create our health and our reality with every thought, every word and every action we take. Our thoughts affect our words; our words affect our actions, and our actions create our reality.

Over the next 12 weeks, you'll begin to become aware of the thoughts and behaviours that are either empowering you or disempowering you. Then you can begin to upgrade them to healthy and constructive behaviours that support your new Rocking Fit® lifestyle. Even if you're already fit and healthy, there is always room for an upgrade.

Your starting point involves being honest with yourself and taking responsibility for all your past choices. No matter where you are on your health and fitness journey, you can't make progress if you're still beating yourself up for poor food choices or laziness. You have to accept your past choices, come into the present moment and start exactly where you are. The exciting part, is that you have the power to make a new choice in every new moment and move beyond past limitations and perceived failures.

Working out and eating well are only two aspects of a Rocking Fit® body. Although this is a 12-week training plan, you'll need to stop thinking short term and start thinking lifestyle if you want to make real progress. To successfully reach your goals and maintain your fitness, you're going to need to think beyond diet and exercise and see your life holistically.

As you think healthy, positive thoughts and go within to connect to your true power, you will naturally make healthier, more positive choices that serve your highest good. The mind, body and spirit are connected and all lasting transformations happen when we work from the inside out.

Purpose, Potential & Bliss

Creating an inspiring purpose for your life is the fuel you need to move you from where you are to where you want to go.

The key to goal achievement is creating an exciting purpose for your life, one that motivates and excites you. When you have an inspiring purpose for getting fit, beyond how you look in the mirror, you'll find an enthusiasm for life that perhaps you've never had before. Fitness then simply becomes a vehicle for achieving your purpose.

When you live on purpose, no one or nothing can stop you. You know where you're going and what you need to do; no challenge, difficulty or obstacle can get in your way. People start to notice your incredible energy and you begin to not only transform your life but also the lives of those around you. When you live on purpose, you can see the big picture and suddenly it's not all about your life but how you can contribute to a better world by making yourself a better person. When you live on purpose, you're excited by what's possible, you let go of fear, anxiety and procrastination and easily achieve your goal, and it becomes a snowball effect.

The better you feel, the more energy you have, the more energy you have, the more able you are to pursue your bigger goals. When you pursue your big goals, life starts to feel fun, you feel more confident and in turn you get better results. As you fulfill your purpose and unlock more of your body and mind's potential, you'll naturally feel happier, content and even blissful.

You've probably heard the quote "follow your bliss". Well, it's true! Make sure you're following your bliss because it really is the secret to a happy life.

True happiness comes through reaching for your potential.

The Journey

I'll be honest, the next 12 weeks is going to be a lot of fun, a lot of hard work and probably quite challenging at times. There are going to be days when you feel great, bouncing out of bed, excited to do your workout. There are also going to be days when you won't feel so great. Life might get in the way, you may feel tired, your kids might get sick, work might become too much -- and there may be many excuses for why you think can't finish this program. I want you to take a moment now to acknowledge that voice so you can recognise it. Instead of giving into it, during the next 12 weeks you're going to make a newly empowered choice. That choice comes down to self-love and answering the question, "Do I believe I'm worth it?"

This 12-week journey will inspire and motivate you to take massive action towards your fitness goals. You're going to become more conscious of your strengths, your weaknesses or where you might be sabotaging yourself. As you see your transformation unfold, you'll be inspired to keep going, and by committing to your workouts and The 8 Daily Steps, you'll gain even more momentum and overcome resistance and excuses that may have held you back in the past.

As you work on your mindset as well as your training, your thoughts and actions will become congruent. As you come into full alignment, you'll begin to see amazing upgrades to your health, wellness, motivation and your ability to easily achieve your goals. Even the smallest of new choices can create huge upgrades to the quality of your life.

You'll notice I like to use the word "upgrade" instead of words like fix, improve or change. The idea is that we don't need to "fix" anything. Your Rocking Fit® body is already within you—it just needs to be revealed. From now on, let's agree to use the word "upgrade" when we talk about changing or improving anything. Upgrading your thoughts, beliefs, and behaviours results in empowered thinking, healthy choices, productive actions and achieving your health and fitness goals.

Rituals, Habits and Magic

Forming a new habit takes time. To successfully integrate any new habit into your daily routine, it's useful to create a ritual. Working with your journal and creating a workout schedule around the same time each day increases your chance of success. Give yourself the best chance by putting your Dailygreatness Training Journal by your bed, on your work desk, in your kitchen or somewhere that you will see it easily. Keeping it close by will help you follow through and stay on track. Don't put it on the bookshelf and forget about it! Magic happens when you stay committed, focused and keep your promises.

Try this! Right now, grab a pen and paper, pour yourself a coffee and sit down in your favourite comfy chair. Now you're going to write a letter to your future Rocking Fit® self. Describe clearly how you want to feel, what you want to look like and what you want to achieve in the next 12 weeks. Write it now, seal it in an envelope, write the date on the front and mark your diary to read it in 12 weeks time. Once you've completed the journal, you will go back and read this letter and see how many goals you've accomplished, how you feel and how much you've progressed.

Self-Mastery, Bad Habits and Self-Sabotage

Self-mastery and the attainment of your goals go hand in hand. The steps, tools and questions throughout this journal are designed to gently guide you in achieving self-awareness and increased self-mastery. Becoming more positive in our attitudes is definitely one aspect to self-mastery, however, focusing only on the positive can limit our ability to achieve our goals and live authentically.

True transformation happens when we are courageous enough to face our fears, acknowledge our weaknesses and question our negative beliefs.

These unconscious thinking patterns lie hidden in our subconscious mind until something triggers them to pop up and sabotage our best intentions.

It takes willingness, persistence and committed effort to recognise and remove these patterns that no longer serve you. While it can be uncomfortable to look at these aspects of ourselves, it really is the only way to grow. All our potential lies in the unconscious part of our mind, waiting for us to shine a light on it. If you stay focused, you can use these revelations as steppingstones to become free from procrastination, release old patterns and practising self-love instead of self-sabotage. Old habits die hard, and as we confront our fears, our unconscious patterns often rise to the surface so we can finally face them before consciously letting them go.

Be brave, thank your old habits for their incredible lessons and gifts that they've given you, and keep moving forward.

Falling off the Wagon

It's easy to start out strong on a new adventure, but harder to stay inspired after the initial excitement has worn off. You'll probably hit a few dips and bumps, miss a few days of training, maybe even have a blowout and eat some junk food along the way. If you do, don't worry. It's okay! The next 12 weeks and beyond is not about being perfect; it's about being conscious of the choices you make.

Simply acknowledge any issues that come up and ask yourself a few questions, like:

What triggered me to skip my training session?
What made me reach for that chocolate/ice cream/candy?
Am I still inspired by my purpose and goals?
What fears are holding me back?
Why am I procrastinating?
What am I choosing to focus on?
What do I need to start or stop?
What don't I want, and what would I prefer?

Use your answers to empower yourself and make adjustments to your plans and goals and then re-commit to your Rocking Fit® lifestyle!

Who Are Your Five Closest Friends?

Surrounding yourself with positive people who support your new Rocking Fit® lifestyle is essential during your 12-week transformation and beyond.

Your environment and external influences play a huge role in your ability to achieve and sustain your fitness goals. If you're not currently surrounded by people who have goals, dreams and values similar to yours, then maybe it's time to find a community of people who do. In short, hang out with and learn from people who inspire you, uplift you, empower you and support you.

You Can Do This!

I'm not telling
you it's going to
be easy, I'm telling
you it's going to be
worth it.

The 8 Daily Steps: Your Foundation to a Rocking Fit Body, Mind & Spirit

The 8 Daily Steps are designed to be short, focused sessions that you do first thing in the morning and last thing at night to keep you on track and motivated towards achieving your goals. Think of your daily practice as the foundation for reinventing yourself one thought, one intention, one push-up, one healthy meal at a time.

It may feel overwhelming at first when looking at the big picture and considering how to incorporate these new 8 steps into your daily routine. In the beginning, you may want to go slowly by adding a new step every few days until you get used to the routine of all 8 Daily Steps.

How you choose to use the journal and how much time you spend on each step is entirely up to you.

I recommend a minimum of 30 minutes for the morning session, plus 25-45 minutes for your workout. Then a minimum of 15 minutes for your evening Self-Awareness Power Questions. That's approximately 1.5hrs per day, which, if you think about it, is *nothing* compared to the many benefits that this program will bring to your life.

Though I recommend following this morning and evening framework, feel free to use your Training Journal any time you need a little extra inspiration or a boost during your day.

At first, it may seem like nothing is happening and that the journal and training are not working. Don't be concerned if you don't see any visible results for the first 4 weeks, this is normal.

Whatever you do, don't give up! Continue, push through your resistance and soon you will have breakthroughs in your mindset, your confidence, your self-belief and your health and fitness.

1. Meditation

There's no better place to start a body, mind, spirit transformation, than with Meditation. Practising meditation in the morning is a powerful way to reduce stress, build your character, raise your vibration and stay focused on your goals. Meditation is the ultimate mental trainer and the perfect complement to your fitness training. Meditation need not be mysterious or complicated; simply sit in a comfortable position, allow yourself to become relaxed, centered and present, and focus on your breath. Whenever your mind wanders (and it will!), just bring it right back to your next breath. Start with just 5, 10 or 15 minutes twice a day and over time you'll find you can sit for longer periods. Suggestion: Make 25 minutes your goal or longer, if you can. Something magical happens at the 25 minute mark. See Appendix i for instructions on basic meditation technique.

2. Gratitude

Rock your attitude with gratitude! Gratitude is a powerful emotion that opens you up to being in flow with the universe. It gives you perspective and the much-needed inner energy to pursue your goals and dreams. When we focus on the positive and what's going well, we feel great! Start your day in a state of gratitude by writing down everything you're grateful for each day on your daily gratitude list. It may be as simple as the clothes you're wearing, access to clean fresh water or the ability to train your body. Be grateful for things that are still coming, like your new Rocking Fit® body and feeling confident in a bikini next summer! Remember, whatever you focus on, you will attract more of.

3. Intention

Intention is your point of focus, your mindset, and what you intend to be, do or have in any given moment. Your intention is your underlying motivation and, more than anything else, is responsible for the results you get in life. Every positive thought attracts, every negative thought repels, and each new day is a new opportunity to create your Rocking Fit® lifestyle. Stating your intentions each morning creates a powerful foundation from which to launch your day. Consciously choosing your intentions each morning, will direct your energy so that you can stay focused, no matter what is happening around you. An intention can be a word, personal value or an affirmation starting with "I AM" that directs and confirms your energy and your focus. Some examples are: I AM focused, I AM healthy, I AM achieving my goals. It's important to feel your intention in your body as you state it aloud. Saying it aloud as well as feeling it, will anchor the energy of your intention into your body's cellular memory. Stating your intentions is a powerful way to attract into your energy field all that you want. Be sure to choose your intentions carefully, because they will become your reality!

4. Eat Clean

If you really want to hit your ideal weight, tone up your tummy and reach your fitness goals, you'll need to clean up your diet. Unfortunately, there are no shortcuts. More than fifty percent of the results you get over the next 12 weeks will come from the food you choose to eat. Think of food as fuel. What you put in, you get out. You need good fuel to optimise your energy. Eating clean, healthy foods that fuel your active lifestyle is essential if you plan on completing this 12-week program. If you workout a lot but have a poor diet, you will fail. When you choose the right foods, you feel focused, energised, enthusiastic and willing to take on the day. Poor food choices weigh you down, affect your mood and sleeping patterns and leave you feeling unmotivated, depressed and in the worst case, create disease in your body. A diet high in lean protein, fruit, vegetables, whole grains and healthy fats is the key to weight loss, building muscle, having high energy, and a balanced blood sugar level. It's very important not to skip meals. Don't get sucked into thinking you need to starve yourself to lose weight. It doesn't work that way; you need to eat! A big part of eating well is planning well. Do your shopping and plan your meals every Sunday using the Weekly Planner. Every morning prepare your meals for the day and try to have a protein shake within one hour of your training session. Your goal with this step is to eat five to six small proportioned high protein meals every three hours. Then log each meal and snack on your Daily Meal Planner and get ready for a Rocking Fit® bikini body!

5. Intensity Training

Training doesn't have to mean long boring workouts in the gym. To avoid plateauing or dying of boredom, step up the intensity by shocking your body with some new and fun workouts that you've never done before. Instead of focusing on inches, weight and body fat percentages, during your days simply focus on moving your body as much as possible and having fun! When you start thinking of your training as play, then you'll want to do it more often. If you don't love it, you won't do it. The key to effective training lies in the intensity, variety and consistency of your workouts. As with any new training program, you need to listen to your body. Only after you build strength and improve your fitness, should you begin to increase the intensity of your workouts. While you don't want to over-train, you also don't want to under-train. Finding your edge means training as hard as you can while maintaining good form. Your goal during these 12 weeks is to train with intensity, three to four times per week always with a rest day in between. For the fastest results, the best kind of training is short, intense sessions of 25-45 minutes. Record your training sessions on your Daily Planner by noting the exercise, time, reps, weight and intensity, as well as any notes about how you felt during and after your workout. If you're on a rest day, simply write: rest day. Get creative and plan exciting training sessions that inspire and challenge you. If you need more inspiration, we can deliver you 12 weeks of amazing workouts that you can do right from the comfort of your home at www.rockingfit.com.

6. Water

Drinking lots of water is the next piece in the holistic wellness puzzle. Staying hydrated is not just important for training, it is a key element for slimming down, toning up and maintaining your energy. First thing in the morning, kick start your metabolism with a big glass of cool water. Keep a water bottle with you or on your desk at work during the day to remind yourself to keep drinking. Adding some fresh lemon to your water is a great way to get your body into an alkaline state. While you're training, keep sipping your water before, during and after your workouts to maximize your energy and aid your recovery. You might also want to consider quitting tea, coffee or other caffeine products that dehydrate you. Yes, unfortunately, that means chocolate, too! Your goal is to drink at least 1.5 liters or 8 glasses of water a day. Use the tick box on the Daily Planner as a reminder to stay hydrated and get ready to look and feel like a firm, juicy peach!

7. Stretching

Stretching is often undervalued and, therefore, many times is skipped at the start or end of a workout. However, gaining flexibility by stretching our body is just as, if not more, important, as strength training, cardio or any other part of your workout. As we get older and less active, exercise becomes more difficult due to stiffness and tightening of our muscles and joints. Stretching helps us stay strong and supple, improves our mobility, prevents injury and maintains our posture. Many people complain that they are not more flexible, but anyone can achieve more flexibility, it just takes practice. Always remember to do a good pre-workout warm up, by stretching your major muscle groups. After your workout, give yourself the gift of a long and deep full-body stretch and see how your mind and body transform. Make it your goal to master the art of stretching and get used to bending forward and saying hello to your toes as often as possible!

8. Evening Power Questions

Each evening, you will have the opportunity to answer three Self-Awareness Power Questions to reflect, debrief and evaluate your day. Reflecting on your day and asking self-awareness questions is a powerful process that activates your internal search engine to come up with new possibilities and solutions to your challenges. Through asking yourself a series of questions, you will begin to discover new ways to live a healthier, empowered, and self-honest life. The better your questions, the better your answers. Throughout the Dailygreatness Training Journal, you'll find many Self-Awareness Questions, but don't limit yourself to these. Challenge yourself to come up with intelligent questions that trigger the answers you're searching for. Once you've answered the evening questions, spend time scheduling your training sessions, your food plan and setting your intentions for the day ahead using the Daily Planner. This process will clear your mind, give you a clear vision of your day ahead and set you up for maximum success from the moment your feet hit the floor.

If it doesn't challenge you, it doesn't change you.

Fred Devito

Rocking Body Blueprint

Your Rocking Body Blueprint highlights where you are now and where you want to be in the eight areas of fitness. It gives you a clear vision of where you are going and one massive action to take towards achieving your goal. You'll be prompted to come back to your Rocking Body Blueprint throughout the 12 weeks to check and celebrate your progress.

12 Week Goal Planner

The 12 Week Goal Planner gives you the opportunity to create three major fitness goals per month over the next 12 weeks and gives you an outline for achieving them. When creating your goals, be specific by setting a target date for each goal. Then, use the questions to get clear on what you want, why you want it, how will you make it happen, when you will have it and how you will feel once you've reached your goal.

Tip: A great way to visualise your goals and stay inspired is to put together a beautiful vision board that serves as a dynamic visual reminder and keeps your fitness goals fresh in your mind each day.

12 Week Training Planner

Once you've created your fitness goals, you will then break them down in your 12 Week Training Planner. Your Training Planner is a simple but powerful tool that is essential for staying organized, committed and accountable.

Having a plan for when you will train is especially helpful for overcoming procrastination, lack of motivation and achieving consistency. Your goal is to train three to four times a week with a rest day in between.

Remember, training doesn't have to be boring. When creating your 12 Week Training Plan get creative and make your schedule fun by including a variety of weights, cardio, swimming, yoga, group sports, hiking, biking and climbing. When you enjoy it, you're more likely to do it!

Quick Note: All these instructions might seem a little overwhelming right now, but soon it will all make perfect sense. Just relax and let the pages of the journal guide you.

The Check-Ins

The Weekly, Monthly and 12 Week Check-Ins are designed to help you stay motivated, committed and focused. They highlight the areas of your life that need attention by bringing them into your conscious awareness and support you in upgrading your disempowering habits into empowering ones.

Every Sunday during your Weekly Check-In, you'll have the opportunity to reflect back over the past week and decide what's working and what isn't. By bringing the areas of training, diet and your mindset into focus, you'll then be able to make adjustments and recommit to your goals for the coming week.

The "Get Some Altitude" scale during the Weekly Check-In highlights how your attitude is serving you. The scale represents different levels of your emotional state: 1 is the lowest, where you're feeling completely disempowered, and 10 is the highest, where you're feeling fully empowered. Over the course of the next 12 weeks, make it your intention to move further and further up the scale by becoming aware of your attitudes and feelings and how they affect your life. Creating a winning attitude will help enormously towards staying focused and achieving your goal of a Rocking Fit® lifestyle.

Every Sunday as you work through your weekly planner, you'll get a clear view of your week's training sessions, fitness goals, appointments, projects and plans. Now is also a good time to review your 12 Week Goal Planner to keep yourself moving in the direction of your goals.

Every four weeks, you'll have a 4 Week Check-In where you'll review your past month and reset your focus for the next month. You'll be prompted to take a photo of yourself to record your progress. Then you'll answer a series of questions to identify what you'd like to work on for the next four weeks and celebrate your achievements so far.

At the end of the 12 weeks, you'll have your 12 Week Review. This final review is designed to reflect back on and celebrate your achievements, to learn from your challenges and to consolidate your progress, before launching into another 12-week body transformation!

Tip: Although this journal is filled with useful planners to help you prepare and take action on your goals, it's important not to forget about your training sessions and your inner work. Resist using the journal solely as a diary or planner, since all 8 Daily Steps are essential to achieving your goals and a Rocking Fit® lifestyle.

I'm letting go
of thoughts
that do not
make me
strong.

My Rocking Body Inspiration

Here's your chance to inspire yourself towards your Rocking Fit® body. In the first frame, place a current photo of yourself. In the second frame, find an image of a body that inspires you and that you'd love to have. Come back to this page any time you need inspiration, when you're tempted to reach for a chocolate bar or to celebrate your progress. At the end of 12 weeks, you'll add another picture of your Rocking Fit® body. Remember to have fun with this -- you'll be amazed at your 12-week body transformation if you stick with it.

My Body Now

your photo

My Weight

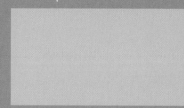

My Measurements

My Rocking Fit Body

your photo

My Weight

My Measurements

Forgiveness sets you free

The leaping off point for a Rocking Fit® lifestyle starts with forgiveness. You can't successfully move forward in life & create a healthy body and mind if you're living with guilt, resentment or regret. Is there someone or something you need to forgive so you can move forward with your life and your health and wellness goals? It could be a person, an event, a failed business, a lost dream or a broken relationship. How about some self-forgiveness? Most times that's usually the best place to start. Anything you've invested your energy in, uses up your precious life force. Now is the time to forgive and let it go. A great way to do that is to write yourself, or someone else, a letter that you never post. Others don't need to know that you're forgiving them for this to be effective. Forgiveness happens inside you. The most important thing is to stop holding the pain in your body and your mind. Use this exercise to free yourself and to reclaim your energy, your power and your potential so you can put everything you have into creating your Rocking Fit® lifestyle.

My Achievements

Sometimes we need to remember how great we already are. Years go by and we lose track of our achievements, and how much we've grown and become. We focus on our "failures" and the negative experiences overshadow the highlights. It's time now to be honest with yourself and see yourself with a renewed perspective. Start with your childhood and do a full inventory, consolidating your life achievements to date, no matter how small they might seem now. Consider a time when you were at your fittest. How did it feel? What about a time you felt proud of yourself? Keep writing until you have listed all those moments. Each month, come back and update this page with your latest and greatest achievements.

....
....
....
....
....
....
....
....
....
....
....
....
....
....
....
....
....
....
....
....
....
....
....
....
....
....
....
....

My Values

Values are your compass that point you towards what really matters to you. They are the underlying motivation for all your choices in life. Identifying your core values is an important step in reaching your goals. When your head and heart are aligned, you will easily achieve your goals, as if by magic. Start by identifying your core values from the list below, then circle your top five. If none of these resonate, write down your own in the space below. Use these as your motivation and your purpose for getting the Rocking Fit® body you want and deserve!

Adventure	Fulfillment	Kindness	Self-reliance
Balance	Forgiveness	Knowledge	Service
Confidence	Fun	Love	Spirituality
Control	God	Lifestyle	Strength
Creativity	Growth	Marriage	Success
Discipline	Happiness	Peace of mind	Truth
Education	Health	Power	Unity
Faith	Hope	Progress	Wealth
Family	Honesty	Reason	Wisdom
Financial Security	Humour	Respect	
Friends	Independence	Security	
Freedom	Integrity	Self-expression	

What matters to me most is: ....
....
....
....
....
....
....
....
....
....
....
....
....
....

My Dreams

Now is your opportunity to let go of fear, to let your imagination run wild and to simply dream. Your dreams are meant to excite you! When you have a big enough dream, one that you're excited to achieve, that excitement becomes the fuel you need to motivate you to achieve what you've always wanted in life. Answer the following questions to reignite your ability to dream and to explore what's really possible:

What is really possible? ....
....
....
....
.... What will change when I am super fit and healthy?
....
....
....
.... When I have the body I want, I'm going to ....
....
....
....
.... What have I always wished for in my life? ....
....
....
.... At the end of these 12 weeks, I am going to feel..............
....
....
....
.... What would I love to be, do or have? ....
....
....
.................If money or time wasn't an issue, and I knew I couldn't fail, what would I do?..
....
....
....

My Goals

Goals are our dreams broken down into achievable actions with a deadline. They give our life meaning, a sense of purpose and a feeling of fulfilment. The secret to setting and achieving goals is knowing why you want something. If you can't come up with a strong enough why or purpose for wanting your goal, then you won't have the motivation to overcome all the challenges and obstacles that you'll meet along the way. Your why comes from your core values and what's most important to you. If your goals aren't congruent with your core values, you'll continually sabotage yourself – or you may achieve your goal, but you won't be able to sustain it. Goals can be big or small, but most of all, they must be meaningful to you or you won't have the drive to achieve them. When creating your fitness goals, be specific and set a deadline for each goal. Answer the following questions to get clear on what you truly want to achieve at the end of these 12 weeks:

What do I want?
Why do I want it?
How will I make it happen?
What are the actions I need to take?
When will I have it?
Who do I need to be to achieve my goals?
Which fears and limiting beliefs do I need to let go of to reach this goal?

....
....
....
....
....
....
....
....
....
....
....
....
....
....
....
....
....
....
....

The difference between the body you have and the body you want is simply the choices you make.

Purpose Statement

Your Purpose Statement is a clear and concise statement summing up the reasons behind wanting your goals. Your purpose is the fuel that fires your inner motivation and becomes the driving force behind all your choices, actions and behaviours.

Answer the following questions to help you uncover your purpose:

Who am I and why am I here? What legacy do I want to leave? What gifts and talents do I wish to share with the world? What have I learnt in my life that I can pass on to others? What is my message? What makes me come alive? What does life want from me? What is it that wants to be expressed through me?

An example of a Purpose Statement would be: "To reach my body's potential and have more energy for my husband and kids."

Personal Fitness Statement

Your Personal Fitness Statement is a paragraph that clearly states how you will achieve your fitness goals.

Both your Purpose Statement and Personal Fitness Statement will change and evolve as you do, so don't worry too much about getting it perfect right away. Instead, think of it as fluid and changing and feel free to tweak and update it as you get more clear on your purpose. As you move through the 12 weeks, you'll be prompted to read your statements regularly, and as you do, you'll find yourself embodying the thoughts and behaviours of your future fit self.

An example of a Personal Fitness Statement might be: "Through daily commitment, focus, self-love and keeping promises to myself, I will courageously let go of self-sabotaging habits and create the Rocking Fit® lifestyle I deserve, and I'm going to feel amazing doing it!"

Of course, it could be much simpler or more complex than this.

The Pillars of Success

Potential

PURPOSE PLANNING

CONSISTENCY **ENDURANCE**

FLEXIBILITY Hydration

SELF-HONESTY **STRENGTH**

Persistence *Rest* **VARIETY**

DISCIPLINE **FOCUS** *Intensity*

SELF-LOVE *FUN* **DETERMINATION**

My Rocking Body Blueprint

	Where I Am Now	My 12 Week Goal	One Massive Action Towards That Goal
Weight			
Diet & Hydration			
Discipline			
Endurance			
Strength			
Flexibility			
Self-Love			
Rest			

Strength doesn't come from what you can do. It comes from overcom- ing the things you once thought you couldn't do.

Rikki Rogers

12 Week Goal Planner

Weeks 1 - 4

Fitness Goal:	Fitness Goal:	Fitness Goal:
Target date:	Target date:	Target date:
How I'm going to achieve this goal:	How I'm going to achieve this goal:	How I'm going to achieve this goal:
1.	1.	1.
2.	2.	2.
3.	3.	3.
4.	4.	4.
Why I'd love to achieve this goal:	Why I'd love to achieve this goal:	Why I'd love to achieve this goal:
How will I feel when I've reached this goal?	How will I feel when I've reached this goal?	How will I feel when I've reached this goal?

Weeks 5 - 8

Fitness Goal:	Fitness Goal:	Fitness Goal:
Target date:	Target date:	Target date:
How I'm going to achieve this goal:	How I'm going to achieve this goal:	How I'm going to achieve this goal:
1.	1.	1.
2.	2.	2.
3.	3.	3.
4.	4.	4.
Why I'd love to achieve this goal:	Why I'd love to achieve this goal:	Why I'd love to achieve this goal:
How will I feel when I've reached this goal?	How will I feel when I've reached this goal?	How will I feel when I've reached this goal?

Weeks 9 - 12

Fitness Goal:	Fitness Goal:	Fitness Goal:
Target date:	Target date:	Target date:
How I'm going to achieve this goal:	How I'm going to achieve this goal:	How I'm going to achieve this goal:
1.	1.	1.
2.	2.	2.
3.	3.	3.
4.	4.	4.
Why I'd love to achieve this goal:	Why I'd love to achieve this goal:	Why I'd love to achieve this goal:
How will I feel when I've reached this goal?	How will I feel when I've reached this goal?	How will I feel when I've reached this goal?

12 Week Training Planner

	Monday	Tuesday	Wednesday
Week 1			
Week 2			
Week 3			
Week 4			

	Monday	Tuesday	Wednesday
Week 5			
Week 6			
Week 7			
Week 8			

	Monday	Tuesday	Wednesday
Week 9			
Week 10			
Week 11			
Week 12			

Thursday	Friday	Saturday	Sunday

Thursday	Friday	Saturday	Sunday

Thursday	Friday	Saturday	Sunday

The difference between where you are now and where you want to be is what you do.

Today I would love...
_____
_____
_____
_____
_____

Date

Meditation   8 Glasses of Water

Stretching   ....

Today I am so grateful for...

Breakfast:

Snack:

Lunch:

Snack:

Dinner:

Snack:

My intentions for today are...

Post-training protein:

I AM
I AM
I AM

6.00

7.00

Workout:

Time/Duration:

8.00

Distance:

Intensity Level 1-10:

9.00

Reps/Weight:

Sequence:

10.00

Intervals:

What I Noticed:

11.00

Notes for Next Session:

12.00

Recovery Notes:

13.00

What did I learn today?

14.00

15.00

After today, what behaviour do I want to upgrade?

16.00

17.00

What strengths did I use today?

18.00

19.00

☐ Meditation ☐ 8 Glasses of Water

☐ Stretching ☐ ....

Breakfast:

Snack:

Lunch:

Snack:

Dinner:

Snack:

Post-training protein:

6.00

7.00

8.00

9.00

10.00

11.00

12.00

13.00

14.00

15.00

16.00

17.00

18.00

19.00

What if (insert possibility)...

Date

Today I'm going to appreciate...

The mindset I wish to create today is...

I AM

I AM

I AM

Workout:

Time/Duration:

Distance:

Intensity Level 1-10:

Reps/Weight:

Sequence:

Intervals:

What I Noticed:

Notes for Next Session:

Recovery Notes:

What did I enjoy about today?

What challenged me today that I can grow from?

What did I do really well today?

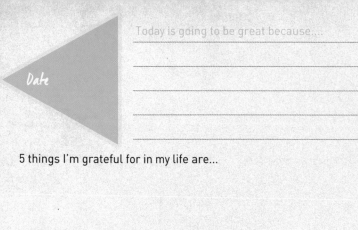

Today is going to be great because....

_____

_____

_____

_____

Date

Meditation   8 Glasses of Water

Stretching   ....

Breakfast:

Snack:

Lunch:

Snack:

Dinner:

Snack:

Post-training protein:

5 things I'm grateful for in my life are...

Today I am focusing on being...

I AM

I AM

I AM

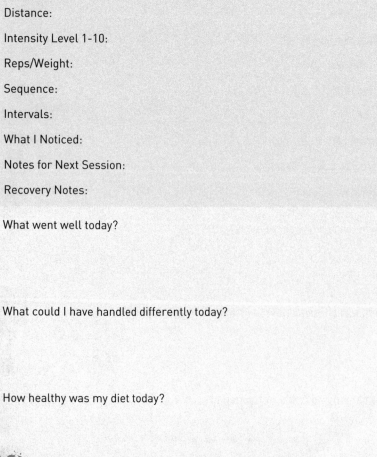

Workout:

Time/Duration:

Distance:

Intensity Level 1-10:

Reps/Weight:

Sequence:

Intervals:

What I Noticed:

Notes for Next Session:

Recovery Notes:

What went well today?

What could I have handled differently today?

How healthy was my diet today?

6.00

7.00

8.00

9.00

10.00

11.00

12.00

13.00

14.00

15.00

16.00

17.00

18.00

19.00

□ Meditation □ 8 Glasses of Water

□ Stretching □ ....

Date

Breakfast:

Snack:

Lunch:

Snack:

Dinner:

Snack:

Post-training protein:

I am so grateful for these people in my life...

I create my day with my thoughts, therefore...

I AM

I AM

I AM

Workout:

Time/Duration:

Distance:

Intensity Level 1-10:

Reps/Weight:

Sequence:

Intervals:

What I Noticed:

Notes for Next Session:

Recovery Notes:

What did I love about today?

What would I like to let go of?

How can I make tomorrow better than today?

6.00

7.00

8.00

9.00

10.00

11.00

12.00

13.00

14.00

15.00

16.00

17.00

18.00

19.00

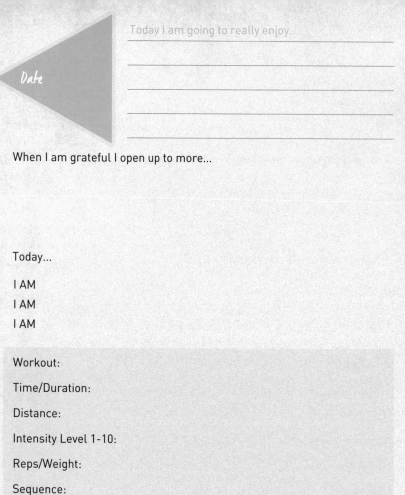

Today I am going to really enjoy...

_____
_____
_____
_____
_____

Date

Meditation   8 Glasses of Water

Stretching   ....

Breakfast:

Snack:

Lunch:

Snack:

Dinner:

Snack:

Post-training protein:

When I am grateful I open up to more...

Today...

I AM

I AM

I AM

Workout:

Time/Duration:

Distance:

Intensity Level 1-10:

Reps/Weight:

Sequence:

Intervals:

What I Noticed:

Notes for Next Session:

Recovery Notes:

What was interesting about today?

What habit would I like to develop after today?

What strengths did I use today?

6.00

7.00

8.00

9.00

10.00

11.00

12.00

13.00

14.00

15.00

16.00

17.00

18.00

19.00

■ Meditation ■ 8 Glasses of Water

■ Stretching ■ ....

Breakfast:

Snack:

Lunch:

Snack:

Dinner:

Snack:

Post-training protein:

6.00

7.00

8.00

9.00

10.00

11.00

12.00

13.00

14.00

15.00

16.00

17.00

18.00

19.00

Today is my opportunity to...

_____

_____

_____

_____

_____

Today, I give thanks for...

Today I honour how I feel and...

I AM

I AM

I AM

Workout:

Time/Duration:

Distance:

Intensity Level 1-10:

Reps/Weight:

Sequence:

Intervals:

What I Noticed:

Notes for Next Session:

Recovery Notes:

What was today's lesson?

What new behaviour can I adopt into my life?

What did I suceed at today?

Date

Weekly Check-in

	09.00	12.00	15.00
	10.00	13.00	16.00
	11.00	14.00	17.00

What have I achieved this week?

What's working and why is it working?

What's not working and what am I willing to do to upgrade it?

What is one thing I can do this week that will create the biggest results towards my fitness goals?

Where is my current attitude on a scale from 1-10? How can I get some more altitude and upgrade my attitude?

Am I being self-honest about my diet and training?

What beliefs are holding me back and how can I upgrade those?

How can I make my training sessions more fun next week?

Rocking Body: One Massive Action

Review 12 Week Goal Planner

My Ideal Body Inspiration

Plan Training & Meals For This Week

Old Habit >

New Habit >

New Actions >

New Affirmation / Mantra

4 Major Goals I'm Focused On This Week:

1	2	3	4

Projects & Appointments For This Week	Time	Training, Stretching & Meals	Time
monday			
tuesday			
wednesday			
thursday			
friday			
saturday			
sunday			

~~Today~~
Every day
is a good
day to
workout.

Today I am open to the possibility of...

_____

_____

_____

_____

_____

Date

Meditation   8 Glasses of Water

Stretching   ....

Breakfast:

Snack:

Lunch:

Snack:

Dinner:

Snack:

Post-training protein:

What I love about my body is...

I have a winning mindset and...

I AM

I AM

I AM

Workout:

Time/Duration:

Distance:

Intensity Level 1-10:

Reps/Weight:

Sequence:

Intervals:

What I Noticed:

Notes for Next Session:

Recovery Notes:

How was my mindset today?

What new habit do I want to adopt into my life?

How did I stay committed to my fitness goals today?

6.00

7.00

8.00

9.00

10.00

11.00

12.00

13.00

14.00

15.00

16.00

17.00

18.00

19.00

■ Meditation ■ 8 Glasses of Water

■ Stretching ■ ....

Date

Breakfast:

Snack:

Lunch:

Snack:

Dinner:

Snack:

Post-training protein:

I am so grateful for the simple things like...

Today I am healthy and...

I AM

I AM

I AM

6.00

7.00

8.00

Workout:

Time/Duration:

Distance:

9.00

Intensity Level 1-10:

Reps/Weight:

10.00

Sequence:

Intervals:

11.00

What I Noticed:

Notes for Next Session:

12.00

Recovery Notes:

13.00

What was fantastic about today?

14.00

15.00

How can I drink more water during my days?

16.00

17.00

What negative attitude do I wish to let go of?

18.00

19.00

Today I would love...

_____

_____

_____

_____

Date

Today I am so grateful for...

My intentions for today are...

I AM

I AM

I AM

Workout:

Time/Duration:

Distance:

Intensity Level 1-10:

Reps/Weight:

Sequence:

Intervals:

What I Noticed:

Notes for Next Session:

Recovery Notes:

What did I learn today?

After today, what behaviour do I want to upgrade?

What strengths did I use today?

Meditation ▢   8 Glasses of Water

Stretching ▢   ▢ ....

Breakfast:

Snack:

Lunch:

Snack:

Dinner:

Snack:

Post-training protein:

6.00

7.00

8.00

9.00

10.00

11.00

12.00

13.00

14.00

15.00

16.00

17.00

18.00

19.00

☐ Meditation   ☐ 8 Glasses of Water

☐ Stretching   ☐ ....

Date

Breakfast:

Snack:

Lunch:

Snack:

Dinner:

Snack:

Post-training protein:

Today I'm going to appreciate...

The mindset I wish to create today is...

I AM

I AM

I AM

Workout:

Time/Duration:

Distance:

Intensity Level 1-10:

Reps/Weight:

Sequence:

Intervals:

What I Noticed:

Notes for Next Session:

Recovery Notes:

What did I enjoy about today?

What challenged me today that I can grow from?

What did I do really well today?

6.00

7.00

8.00

9.00

10.00

11.00

12.00

13.00

14.00

15.00

16.00

17.00

18.00

19.00

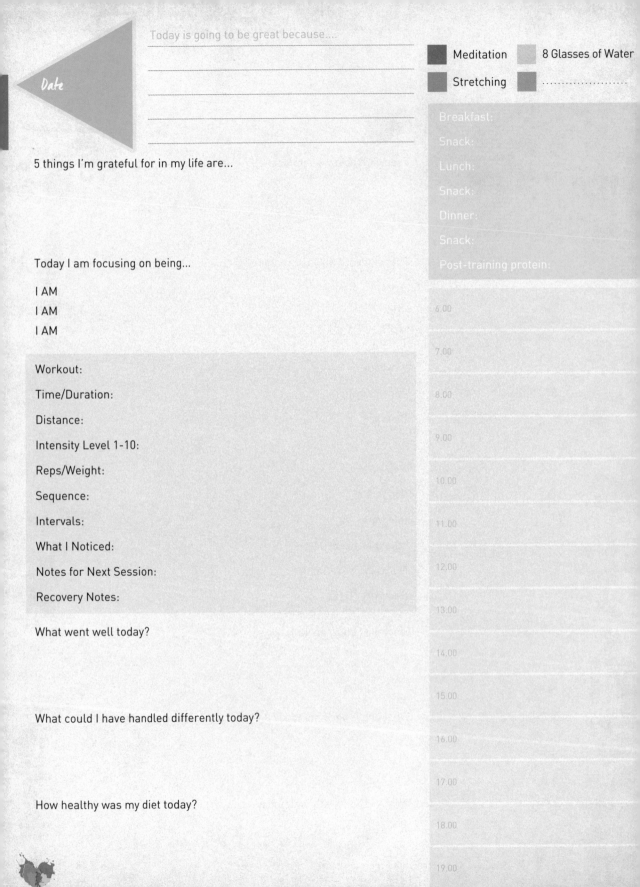

Today is going to be great because....

_____

_____

_____

_____

Date

Meditation   8 Glasses of Water

Stretching   ....

5 things I'm grateful for in my life are...

Breakfast:

Snack:

Lunch:

Snack:

Dinner:

Snack:

Today I am focusing on being...

Post-training protein:

I AM

I AM

I AM

6.00

Workout:

Time/Duration:

Distance:

7.00

Intensity Level 1-10:

Reps/Weight:

8.00

Sequence:

Intervals:

9.00

What I Noticed:

Notes for Next Session:

10.00

Recovery Notes:

11.00

What went well today?

12.00

13.00

14.00

What could I have handled differently today?

15.00

16.00

17.00

How healthy was my diet today?

18.00

19.00

Meditation ☐ 8 Glasses of Water ☐

Stretching ☐ ☐ ....

Breakfast:

Snack:

Lunch:

Snack:

Dinner:

Snack:

Post-training protein:

6.00

7.00

8.00

9.00

10.00

11.00

12.00

13.00

14.00

15.00

16.00

17.00

18.00

19.00

Today I am excited to create...

_____

_____

_____

_____

_____

I am so grateful for these people in my life...

I create my day with my thoughts, therefore...

I AM

I AM

I AM

Workout:

Time/Duration:

Distance:

Intensity Level 1-10:

Reps/Weight:

Sequence:

Intervals:

What I Noticed:

Notes for Next Session:

Recovery Notes:

What did I love about today?

What would I like to let go of?

How can I make tomorrow better than today?

Weekly Check-in

	09.00	12.00	15.00
	10.00	13.00	16.00
	11.00	14.00	17.00

What fitness goals have I completed this week?

What's going well and why is it?

What do I find most challenging about my fitness goals so far?

What is one thing I can do this week that will create
the biggest results in my life?

Where is my current attitude on a scale from 1-10?
How can I get some more altitude and upgrade my attitude?

How can I be more empowered in my thoughts, words and actions?

What fears are holding me back and how can I overcome those?

How does my body feel this week?

Rocking Body: One Massive Action

Review 12 Week Goal Planner

My Ideal Body Inspiration

Plan Training & Meals For This Week

Old Habit >

New Habit >

New Actions >

New Affirmation / Mantra

Weekly Planner

4 Major Goals I'm Focused On This Week:

| 1 | 2 | 3 | 4 |

Projects & Appointments For This Week	Time	Training, Stretching & Meals	Time
monday			
tuesday			
wednesday			
thursday			
friday			
saturday			
sunday			

Don't compete with others, just compete with yourself.

Today I am going to really enjoy...

_____

_____

_____

_____

Date

☐ Meditation   ☐ 8 Glasses of Water

☐ Stretching   ☐ ....

When I am grateful I open up to more...

Breakfast:

Snack:

Lunch:

Snack:

Dinner:

Snack:

Post-training protein:

Today...

I AM

I AM

I AM

Workout:

Time/Duration:

Distance:

Intensity Level 1-10:

Reps/Weight:

Sequence:

Intervals:

What I Noticed:

Notes for Next Session:

Recovery Notes:

What was interesting about today?

6.00

7.00

8.00

9.00

10.00

11.00

12.00

13.00

14.00

15.00

What habit would I like to develop after today?

16.00

17.00

What strengths did I use today?

18.00

19.00

☐ Meditation ☐ 8 Glasses of Water

☐ Stretching ☐ ....

Breakfast:

Snack:

Lunch:

Snack:

Dinner:

Snack:

Post-training protein:

6.00

7.00

8.00

9.00

10.00

11.00

12.00

13.00

14.00

15.00

16.00

17.00

18.00

19.00

Today is my opportunity to...

_____

_____

_____

_____

_____

Date

Today, I give thanks for...

Today I honour how I feel and...

I AM

I AM

I AM

Workout:

Time/Duration:

Distance:

Intensity Level 1-10:

Reps/Weight:

Sequence:

Intervals:

What I Noticed:

Notes for Next Session:

Recovery Notes:

What was today's lesson?

What new behaviour can I adopt into my life?

What did I suceed at today?

Today I am open to the possibility of...

_____

_____

_____

_____

Date

Meditation   8 Glasses of Water

Stretching   ....

Breakfast:

Snack:

Lunch:

Snack:

Dinner:

Snack:

Post-training protein:

What I love about my body is...

I have a winning mindset and...

I AM

I AM

I AM

Workout:

Time/Duration:

Distance:

Intensity Level 1-10:

Reps/Weight:

Sequence:

Intervals:

What I Noticed:

Notes for Next Session:

Recovery Notes:

How was my mindset today?

What new habit do I want to adopt into my life?

How did I stay committed to my fitness goals today?

6.00

7.00

8.00

9.00

10.00

11.00

12.00

13.00

14.00

15.00

16.00

17.00

18.00

19.00

☐ Meditation ☐ 8 Glasses of Water

☐ Stretching ☐ ....

Date

Breakfast:

Snack:

Lunch:

Snack:

Dinner:

Snack:

Post-training protein:

I am so grateful for the simple things like...

Today I am healthy and...

I AM

I AM

I AM

Workout:

Time/Duration:

Distance:

Intensity Level 1-10:

Reps/Weight:

Sequence:

Intervals:

What I Noticed:

Notes for Next Session:

Recovery Notes:

What was fantastic about today?

How can I drink more water during my days?

What negative attitude do I wish to let go of?

6.00

7.00

8.00

9.00

10.00

11.00

12.00

13.00

14.00

15.00

16.00

17.00

18.00

19.00

Today I would love...

Date

Meditation ☐   8 Glasses of Water ☐

Stretching ☐   ☐ ....

Breakfast:

Snack:

Lunch:

Snack:

Dinner:

Snack:

Post-training protein:

Today I am so grateful for...

My intentions for today are...

I AM

I AM

I AM

Workout:

Time/Duration:

Distance:

Intensity Level 1-10:

Reps/Weight:

Sequence:

Intervals:

What I Noticed:

Notes for Next Session:

Recovery Notes:

What did I learn today?

After today, what behaviour do I want to upgrade?

What strengths did I use today?

6.00

7.00

8.00

9.00

10.00

11.00

12.00

13.00

14.00

15.00

16.00

17.00

18.00

19.00

Meditation   8 Glasses of Water

Stretching   ....

Date

Breakfast:

Snack:

Lunch:

Snack:

Dinner:

Snack:

Post-training protein:

Today I'm going to appreciate...

6.00

The mindset I wish to create today is...

I AM

I AM

7.00

I AM

Workout:

8.00

Time/Duration:

Distance:

9.00

Intensity Level 1-10:

Reps/Weight:

10.00

Sequence:

Intervals:

11.00

What I Noticed:

Notes for Next Session:

12.00

Recovery Notes:

13.00

What did I enjoy about today?

14.00

15.00

What challenged me today that I can grow from?

16.00

17.00

What did I do really well today?

18.00

19.00

Weekly Check-in

	09.00	12.00	15.00
	10.00	13.00	16.00
	11.00	14.00	17.00

What have I achieved on my 12 Week Body Blueprint this week?

What do I need to start or stop?

How is my inner dialogue? How can I speak kinder to myself?

What is one thing I can do this week that will create
the biggest results in my life?

Where is my current attitude on a scale from 1-10?
How can I get some more altitude and upgrade my attitude?

How can I be happier and healthier?

What negative attitudes are holding me back and how can I overcome those?

How can I stretch myself further in my training sessions?

Rocking Body: One Massive Action

Review 12 Week Goal Planner

My Ideal Body Inspiration

Plan Training & Meals For This Week

Old Habit >

New Habit >

New Actions >

New Affirmation / Mantra

Weekly Planner

4 Major Goals I'm Focused On This Week:

1	2	3	4

Projects & Appointments For This Week	Time	Training, Stretching & Meals	Time
monday			
tuesday			
wednesday			
thursday			
friday			
saturday			
sunday			

It's amazing
what you can do
when you try.

Today is going to be great because....

_____

_____

_____

_____

Date

 Meditation   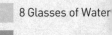 8 Glasses of Water

Stretching   ....

Breakfast:

Snack:

Lunch:

Snack:

Dinner:

Snack:

Post-training protein:

5 things I'm grateful for in my life are...

Today I am focusing on being...

I AM

I AM

I AM

Workout:

Time/Duration:

Distance:

Intensity Level 1-10:

Reps/Weight:

Sequence:

Intervals:

What I Noticed:

Notes for Next Session:

Recovery Notes:

What went well today?

What could I have handled differently today?

How healthy was my diet today?

6.00

7.00

8.00

9.00

10.00

11.00

12.00

13.00

14.00

15.00

16.00

17.00

18.00

19.00

☐ Meditation   ☐ 8 Glasses of Water

☐ Stretching   ☐ ....

Breakfast:

Snack:

Lunch:

Snack:

Dinner:

Snack:

Post-training protein:

6:00

7:00

8:00

9:00

10:00

11:00

12:00

13:00

14:00

15:00

16:00

17:00

18:00

19:00

Today I am excited to create...

Date

I am so grateful for these people in my life...

I create my day with my thoughts, therefore...

I AM

I AM

I AM

Workout:

Time/Duration:

Distance:

Intensity Level 1-10:

Reps/Weight:

Sequence:

Intervals:

What I Noticed:

Notes for Next Session:

Recovery Notes:

What did I love about today?

What would I like to let go of?

How can I make tomorrow better than today?

Today I am going to really enjoy...

Date

Meditation   8 Glasses of Water

Stretching   ....

Breakfast:

Snack:

Lunch:

Snack:

Dinner:

Snack:

Post-training protein:

When I am grateful I open up to more...

Today...

I AM

I AM

I AM

Workout:

Time/Duration:

Distance:

Intensity Level 1-10:

Reps/Weight:

Sequence:

Intervals:

What I Noticed:

Notes for Next Session:

Recovery Notes:

What was interesting about today?

What habit would I like to develop after today?

What strengths did I use today?

6.00

7.00

8.00

9.00

10.00

11.00

12.00

13.00

14.00

15.00

16.00

17.00

18.00

19.00

Meditation	8 Glasses of Water
Stretching	....

Breakfast:

Snack:

Lunch:

Snack:

Dinner:

Snack:

Post-training protein:

6.00

7.00

8.00

9.00

10.00

11.00

12.00

13.00

14.00

15.00

16.00

17.00

18.00

19.00

Today is my opportunity to...

_____

_____

_____

_____

_____

Date

Today, I give thanks for...

Today I honour how I feel and...

I AM

I AM

I AM

Workout:

Time/Duration:

Distance:

Intensity Level 1-10:

Reps/Weight:

Sequence:

Intervals:

What I Noticed:

Notes for Next Session:

Recovery Notes:

What was today's lesson?

What new behaviour can I adopt into my life?

What did I suceed at today?

Today I am open to the possibility of...

_____
_____
_____
_____
_____

Date

| ■ Meditation | □ 8 Glasses of Water |
| ■ Stretching | ■ .... |

What I love about my body is...

Breakfast:

Snack:

Lunch:

Snack:

Dinner:

Snack:

I have a winning mindset and...

Post-training protein:

I AM

I AM

I AM

6.00

Workout:

Time/Duration:

7.00

Distance:

Intensity Level 1-10:

8.00

Reps/Weight:

Sequence:

9.00

Intervals:

What I Noticed:

10.00

Notes for Next Session:

Recovery Notes:

11.00

How was my mindset today?

12.00

13.00

14.00

15.00

What new habit do I want to adopt into my life?

16.00

17.00

How did I stay committed to my fitness goals today?

18.00

19.00

□ Meditation ▢ 8 Glasses of Water

□ Stretching ▢ ....

Breakfast:

Snack:

Lunch:

Snack:

Dinner:

Snack:

Post-training protein:

	6.00
	7.00
	8.00
	9.00
	10.00
	11.00
	12.00
	13.00
	14.00
	15.00
	16.00
	17.00
	18.00
	19.00

Today would be amazing if...

Date

I am so grateful for the simple things like...

Today I am healthy and...

I AM

I AM

I AM

Workout:

Time/Duration:

Distance:

Intensity Level 1-10:

Reps/Weight:

Sequence:

Intervals:

What I Noticed:

Notes for Next Session:

Recovery Notes:

What was fantastic about today?

How can I drink more water during my days?

What negative attitude do I wish to let go of?

4 Week Check-In

Welcome to your 4-Week Check-in! It's time to celebrate your progress, identify what needs attention, record your progress with a photo and reset your focus for the next 4 weeks. Use your answers to the following questions to plan your next month and adjust your goals and training plan accordingly.

What major health goals have I achieved this month?

How can I be more congruent with my thoughts, words and actions?

What are the biggest distractions to my training and how can I remove them?

What is one thing I can do this week that will create the biggest results in my life?

What am I committed to achieving in my life right now?

How can I inspire myself and be inspirational to those around me?

What disempowering thoughts are holding me back and how can I upgrade those?

What fun new exercises can I incorporate into my current training sessions?

Record Your Progress With A Photo   Check 12 Week Goal Planner   Plan Training & Meals For This Week

Review Body Blueprint   Review Purpose & Mission Statement   Celebrate Your Progress!

10 Ways to Get Your Diet Back On Track

1. Drink water like your life depends on it.

2. Fill out your food journal.

3. Don't make up for overeating by not eating.

4. Celebrate small progress.

5. Get used to sweating.

6. Don't let a bad day turn into a bad month.

7. Learn to love vegetables.

8. Learn to say no.

9. Throw out all the naughty food in your fridge and cupboards.

10. Get back to eating five to six small high protein meals per day.

When you look in the mirror & see no change but still keep going....that's the difference between those who succeed & those who fail.

12 Week Goal Planner

Weeks 1 - 4	Fitness Goal:	Fitness Goal:	Fitness Goal:
	Target date:	Target date:	Target date:
	How I'm going to achieve this goal:	How I'm going to achieve this goal:	How I'm going to achieve this goal:
	1.	1.	1.
	2.	2.	2.
	3.	3.	3.
	4.	4.	4.
	Why I'd love to achieve this goal:	Why I'd love to achieve this goal:	Why I'd love to achieve this goal:
	How will I feel when I've reached this goal?	How will I feel when I've reached this goal?	How will I feel when I've reached this goal?

Weeks 5 - 8	Fitness Goal:	Fitness Goal:	Fitness Goal:
	Target date:	Target date:	Target date:
	How I'm going to achieve this goal:	How I'm going to achieve this goal:	How I'm going to achieve this goal:
	1.	1.	1.
	2.	2.	2.
	3.	3.	3.
	4.	4.	4.
	Why I'd love to achieve this goal:	Why I'd love to achieve this goal:	Why I'd love to achieve this goal:
	How will I feel when I've reached this goal?	How will I feel when I've reached this goal?	How will I feel when I've reached this goal?

Weeks 9 - 12	Fitness Goal:	Fitness Goal:	Fitness Goal:
	Target date:	Target date:	Target date:
	How I'm going to achieve this goal:	How I'm going to achieve this goal:	How I'm going to achieve this goal:
	1.	1.	1.
	2.	2.	2.
	3.	3.	3.
	4.	4.	4.
	Why I'd love to achieve this goal:	Why I'd love to achieve this goal:	Why I'd love to achieve this goal:
	How will I feel when I've reached this goal?	How will I feel when I've reached this goal?	How will I feel when I've reached this goal?

4 Major Goals I'm Focused On This Week:

1 **2** **3** **4**

Projects & Appointments For This Week	Time	Training, Stretching & Meals	Time
monday			
tuesday			
wednesday			
thursday			
friday			
saturday			
sunday			

Date

Today I would love...
_____
_____
_____
_____
_____

Today I am so grateful for...

My intentions for today are...

I AM
I AM
I AM

Workout:

Time/Duration:

Distance:

Intensity Level 1-10:

Reps/Weight:

Sequence:

Intervals:

What I Noticed:

Notes for Next Session:

Recovery Notes:

What did I learn today?

After today, what behaviour do I want to upgrade?

What strengths did I use today?

◼ Meditation   ◻ 8 Glasses of Water

◼ Stretching   ◼ ....

Breakfast:

Snack:

Lunch:

Snack:

Dinner:

Snack:

Post-training protein:

6.00

7.00

8.00

9.00

10.00

11.00

12.00

13.00

14.00

15.00

16.00

17.00

18.00

19.00

■ Meditation ■ 8 Glasses of Water

■ Stretching ■ ....

Date

Breakfast:

Snack:

Lunch:

Snack:

Dinner:

Snack:

Post-training protein:

Today I'm going to appreciate...

The mindset I wish to create today is...

I AM

I AM

I AM

6.00	
7.00	
8.00	
9.00	
10.00	
11.00	
12.00	
13.00	
14.00	
15.00	
16.00	
17.00	
18.00	
19.00	

Workout:

Time/Duration:

Distance:

Intensity Level 1-10:

Reps/Weight:

Sequence:

Intervals:

What I Noticed:

Notes for Next Session:

Recovery Notes:

What did I enjoy about today?

What challenged me today that I can grow from?

What did I do really well today?

Today is going to be great because....

_____

_____

_____

_____

■ Meditation   ☐ 8 Glasses of Water

■ Stretching   ■ ....

Breakfast:

Snack:

Lunch:

Snack:

Dinner:

Snack:

Post-training protein:

5 things I'm grateful for in my life are...

Today I am focusing on being...

I AM

I AM

I AM

Workout:

Time/Duration:

Distance:

Intensity Level 1-10:

Reps/Weight:

Sequence:

Intervals:

What I Noticed:

Notes for Next Session:

Recovery Notes:

What went well today?

What could I have handled differently today?

How healthy was my diet today?

6.00

7.00

8.00

9.00

10.00

11.00

12.00

13.00

14.00

15.00

16.00

17.00

18.00

19.00

☐ Meditation   ☐ 8 Glasses of Water

☐ Stretching   ☐ ....

Breakfast:

Snack:

Lunch:

Snack:

Dinner:

Snack:

Post-training protein:

6.00

7.00

8.00

9.00

10.00

11.00

12.00

13.00

14.00

15.00

16.00

17.00

18.00

19.00

Today I am excited to create...

_____

_____

_____

_____

_____

I am so grateful for these people in my life...

I create my day with my thoughts, therefore...

I AM

I AM

I AM

Workout:

Time/Duration:

Distance:

Intensity Level 1-10:

Reps/Weight:

Sequence:

Intervals:

What I Noticed:

Notes for Next Session:

Recovery Notes:

What did I love about today?

What would I like to let go of?

How can I make tomorrow better than today?

Date

Today I am going to really enjoy...

_____
_____
_____
_____
_____

 Meditation  8 Glasses of Water

Stretching ....

When I am grateful I open up to more...

Breakfast:

Snack:

Lunch:

Snack:

Dinner:

Snack:

Post-training protein:

Today...

I AM

I AM

I AM

6.00

Workout:

Time/Duration:

7.00

Distance:

Intensity Level 1-10:

8.00

Reps/Weight:

Sequence:

9.00

Intervals:

What I Noticed:

10.00

Notes for Next Session:

Recovery Notes:

11.00

12.00

What was interesting about today?

13.00

14.00

15.00

What habit would I like to develop after today?

16.00

17.00

What strengths did I use today?

18.00

19.00

Meditation   8 Glasses of Water

Stretching   ....

Breakfast:

Snack:

Lunch:

Snack:

Dinner:

Snack:

Post-training protein:

6.00

7.00

8.00

9.00

10.00

11.00

12.00

13.00

14.00

15.00

16.00

17.00

18.00

19.00

_____

_____

_____

_____

_____

Date

Today, I give thanks for...

Today I honour how I feel and...

I AM

I AM

I AM

Workout:

Time/Duration:

Distance:

Intensity Level 1-10:

Reps/Weight:

Sequence:

Intervals:

What I Noticed:

Notes for Next Session:

Recovery Notes:

What was today's lesson?

What new behaviour can I adopt into my life?

What did I suceed at today?

Weekly Check-in

	09.00	12.00	15.00
	10.00	13.00	16.00
	11.00	14.00	17.00

What fitness goals have I completed this week?

What's going well and why is it?

What do I find most challenging about my fitness goals so far?

What is one thing I can do this week that will create
the biggest results in my life?

Where is my current attitude on a scale from 1-10?
How can I get some more altitude and upgrade my attitude?

How can I be more empowered in my thoughts, words and actions?

What fears are holding me back and how can I overcome those?

How does my body feel this week?

Rocking Body: One Massive Action

Review 12 Week Goal Planner

My Ideal Body Inspiration

Plan Training & Meals For This Week

Old Habit >

New Habit >

New Actions >

New Affirmation / Mantra

Weekly Planner

4 Major Goals I'm Focused On This Week:

1	2	3	4

Projects & Appointments For This Week	Time	Training, Stretching & Meals	Time
monday			
tuesday			
wednesday			
thursday			
friday			
saturday			
sunday			

It doesn't get easier, you get stronger.

Date

Today I am open to the possibility of...

_____

_____

_____

_____

_____

| ■ Meditation | ▢ 8 Glasses of Water |
| ■ Stretching | ▢ .... |

Breakfast:

Snack:

Lunch:

Snack:

Dinner:

Snack:

Post-training protein:

What I love about my body is...

I have a winning mindset and...

I AM

I AM

I AM

Workout:

Time/Duration:

Distance:

Intensity Level 1-10:

Reps/Weight:

Sequence:

Intervals:

What I Noticed:

Notes for Next Session:

Recovery Notes:

How was my mindset today?

What new habit do I want to adopt into my life?

How did I stay committed to my fitness goals today?

6.00

7.00

8.00

9.00

10.00

11.00

12.00

13.00

14.00

15.00

16.00

17.00

18.00

19.00

Meditation   8 Glasses of Water

Stretching   ....

Breakfast:

Snack:

Lunch:

Snack:

Dinner:

Snack:

Post-training protein:

6.00

7.00

8.00

9.00

10.00

11.00

12.00

13.00

14.00

15.00

16.00

17.00

18.00

19.00

I am so grateful for the simple things like...

Today I am healthy and...

I AM

I AM

I AM

Workout:

Time/Duration:

Distance:

Intensity Level 1-10:

Reps/Weight:

Sequence:

Intervals:

What I Noticed:

Notes for Next Session:

Recovery Notes:

What was fantastic about today?

How can I drink more water during my days?

What negative attitude do I wish to let go of?

Date

Date

Today I would love...
_____
_____
_____
_____
_____

Today I am so grateful for...

My intentions for today are...

I AM
I AM
I AM

Workout:

Time/Duration:

Distance:

Intensity Level 1-10:

Reps/Weight:

Sequence:

Intervals:

What I Noticed:

Notes for Next Session:

Recovery Notes:

What did I learn today?

After today, what behaviour do I want to upgrade?

What strengths did I use today?

■ Meditation   ▢ 8 Glasses of Water

■ Stretching   ■ ....

Breakfast:

Snack:

Lunch:

Snack:

Dinner:

Snack:

Post-training protein:

6.00

7.00

8.00

9.00

10.00

11.00

12.00

13.00

14.00

15.00

16.00

17.00

18.00

19.00

- ⬛ Meditation
- ⬛ 8 Glasses of Water
- ⬛ Stretching
- ⬛ ....

Breakfast:

Snack:

Lunch:

Snack:

Dinner:

Snack:

Post-training protein:

6.00

7.00

8.00

9.00

10.00

11.00

12.00

13.00

14.00

15.00

16.00

17.00

18.00

19.00

What if (insert possibility)...

Date

Today I'm going to appreciate...

The mindset I wish to create today is...

I AM

I AM

I AM

Workout:

Time/Duration:

Distance:

Intensity Level 1-10:

Reps/Weight:

Sequence:

Intervals:

What I Noticed:

Notes for Next Session:

Recovery Notes:

What did I enjoy about today?

What challenged me today that I can grow from?

What did I do really well today?

Date

Today is going to be great because....

_____
_____
_____
_____
_____

 Meditation 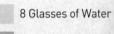 8 Glasses of Water

■ Stretching ■ ....

5 things I'm grateful for in my life are...

Today I am focusing on being...

I AM
I AM
I AM

Workout:

Time/Duration:

Distance:

Intensity Level 1-10:

Reps/Weight:

Sequence:

Intervals:

What I Noticed:

Notes for Next Session:

Recovery Notes:

What went well today?

What could I have handled differently today?

How healthy was my diet today?

Breakfast:

Snack:

Lunch:

Snack:

Dinner:

Snack:

Post-training protein:

6.00

7.00

8.00

9.00

10.00

11.00

12.00

13.00

14.00

15.00

16.00

17.00

18.00

19.00

■ Meditation   ■ 8 Glasses of Water

■ Stretching   ■ ....

Breakfast:

Snack:

Lunch:

Snack:

Dinner:

Snack:

Post-training protein:

6.00

7.00

8.00

9.00

10.00

11.00

12.00

13.00

14.00

15.00

16.00

17.00

18.00

19.00

Today I am excited to create...

_____

_____

_____

_____

_____

Date

I am so grateful for these people in my life...

I create my day with my thoughts, therefore...

I AM

I AM

I AM

Workout:

Time/Duration:

Distance:

Intensity Level 1-10:

Reps/Weight:

Sequence:

Intervals:

What I Noticed:

Notes for Next Session:

Recovery Notes:

What did I love about today?

What would I like to let go of?

How can I make tomorrow better than today?

Weekly Check-in

	09.00	12.00	15.00
	10.00	13.00	16.00
	11.00	14.00	17.00

What have I achieved on my 12 Week Body Blueprint this week?

What do I need to start or stop?

How is my inner dialogue? How can I speak kinder to myself?

What is one thing I can do this week that will create
the biggest results in my life?

Where is my current attitude on a scale from 1-10?
How can I get some more altitude and upgrade my attitude?

How can I be happier and healthier?

What negative attitudes are holding me back and how can I overcome those?

How can I stretch myself further in my training sessions?

Rocking Body: One Massive Action

Review 12 Week Goal Planner

My Ideal Body Inspiration

Plan Training & Meals For This Week

Old Habit >

New Habit >

New Actions >

New Affirmation / Mantra

4 Major Goals I'm Focused On This Week:

1	2	3	4

Projects & Appointments For This Week	Time	Training, Stretching & Meals	Time
monday			
tuesday			
wednesday			
thursday			
friday			
saturday			
sunday			

There are no shortcuts, there is only training hard, eating clean and deciding you can do whatever you put your mind to.

Date

Meditation   8 Glasses of Water

Stretching   ....

Breakfast:

Snack:

Lunch:

Snack:

Dinner:

Snack:

Post-training protein:

When I am grateful I open up to more...

Today...

I AM
I AM
I AM

Workout:

Time/Duration:

Distance:

Intensity Level 1-10:

Reps/Weight:

Sequence:

Intervals:

What I Noticed:

Notes for Next Session:

Recovery Notes:

What was interesting about today?

What habit would I like to develop after today?

What strengths did I use today?

6.00

7.00

8.00

9.00

10.00

11.00

12.00

13.00

14.00

15.00

16.00

17.00

18.00

19.00

■ Meditation ■ 8 Glasses of Water

■ Stretching ■ ....

Date

Breakfast:

Snack:

Lunch:

Snack:

Dinner:

Snack:

Post-training protein:

Today, I give thanks for...

Today I honour how I feel and...

I AM

I AM

I AM

6:00

7:00

8:00

9:00

10:00

11:00

12:00

13:00

14:00

15:00

16:00

17:00

18:00

19:00

Workout:

Time/Duration:

Distance:

Intensity Level 1-10:

Reps/Weight:

Sequence:

Intervals:

What I Noticed:

Notes for Next Session:

Recovery Notes:

What was today's lesson?

What new behaviour can I adopt into my life?

What did I suceed at today?

Today I am open to the possibility of...

Date

_____
_____
_____
_____
_____

Meditation   8 Glasses of Water

Stretching   ....

Breakfast:

Snack:

Lunch:

Snack:

Dinner:

Snack:

Post-training protein:

What I love about my body is...

I have a winning mindset and...

I AM

I AM

I AM

6.00

Workout:

Time/Duration:

Distance:

7.00

Intensity Level 1-10:

8.00

Reps/Weight:

Sequence:

9.00

Intervals:

What I Noticed:

10.00

Notes for Next Session:

11.00

Recovery Notes:

12.00

How was my mindset today?

13.00

14.00

15.00

What new habit do I want to adopt into my life?

16.00

17.00

How did I stay committed to my fitness goals today?

18.00

19.00

■ Meditation   ■ 8 Glasses of Water

■ Stretching   ■ ....

Date

Breakfast:

Snack:

Lunch:

Snack:

Dinner:

Snack:

Post-training protein:

I am so grateful for the simple things like...

Today I am healthy and...

I AM

I AM

I AM

6.00

7.00

8.00

9.00

10.00

11.00

12.00

13.00

14.00

15.00

16.00

17.00

18.00

19.00

Workout:

Time/Duration:

Distance:

Intensity Level 1-10:

Reps/Weight:

Sequence:

Intervals:

What I Noticed:

Notes for Next Session:

Recovery Notes:

What was fantastic about today?

How can I drink more water during my days?

What negative attitude do I wish to let go of?

Date

Today I would love...

_____

_____

_____

_____

_____

| ■ | Meditation | ■ | 8 Glasses of Water |
| ■ | Stretching | ■ | .... |

Breakfast:

Snack:

Lunch:

Snack:

Dinner:

Snack:

Post-training protein:

Today I am so grateful for...

My intentions for today are...

I AM

I AM

I AM

Workout:

Time/Duration:

Distance:

Intensity Level 1-10:

Reps/Weight:

Sequence:

Intervals:

What I Noticed:

Notes for Next Session:

Recovery Notes:

What did I learn today?

After today, what behaviour do I want to upgrade?

What strengths did I use today?

6.00

7.00

8.00

9.00

10.00

11.00

12.00

13.00

14.00

15.00

16.00

17.00

18.00

19.00

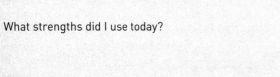

☐ Meditation ☐ 8 Glasses of Water

☐ Stretching ☐ ....

Breakfast:

Snack:

Lunch:

Snack:

Dinner:

Snack:

Post-training protein:

6.00

7.00

8.00

9.00

10.00

11.00

12.00

13.00

14.00

15.00

16.00

17.00

18.00

19.00

What if (insert possibility)...

_____

_____

_____

_____

_____

Date

Today I'm going to appreciate...

The mindset I wish to create today is...

I AM

I AM

I AM

Workout:

Time/Duration:

Distance:

Intensity Level 1-10:

Reps/Weight:

Sequence:

Intervals:

What I Noticed:

Notes for Next Session:

Recovery Notes:

What did I enjoy about today?

What challenged me today that I can grow from?

What did I do really well today?

Weekly Check-in

	09.00	12.00	15.00
	10.00	13.00	16.00
	11.00	14.00	17.00

What have I achieved this week?

What's working and why is it working?

What's not working and what am I willing to do to upgrade it?

What is one thing I can do this week that will create the biggest results towards my fitness goals?

Where is my current attitude on a scale from 1-10?
How can I get some more altitude and upgrade my attitude?

Am I being self-honest about my diet and training?

What beliefs are holding me back and how can I upgrade those?

How can I make my training sessions more fun next week?

Rocking Body: One Massive Action

Review 12 Week Goal Planner

My Ideal Body Inspiration

Plan Training & Meals For This Week

Old Habit >

New Habit >

New Actions >

New Affirmation / Mantra

Weekly Planner

4 Major Goals I'm Focused On This Week:

1

2

3

4

Projects & Appointments For This Week	Time	Training, Stretching & Meals	Time
monday			
tuesday			
wednesday			
thursday			
friday			
saturday			
sunday			

Every
day you
succeed you
get one step
closer to
your goal.

Date

Today is going to be great because....

_____
_____
_____
_____

5 things I'm grateful for in my life are...

Today I am focusing on being...

I AM
I AM
I AM

Workout:

Time/Duration:

Distance:

Intensity Level 1-10:

Reps/Weight:

Sequence:

Intervals:

What I Noticed:

Notes for Next Session:

Recovery Notes:

What went well today?

What could I have handled differently today?

How healthy was my diet today?

☐ Meditation   ☐ 8 Glasses of Water

☐ Stretching   ☐ ....

Breakfast:

Snack:

Lunch:

Snack:

Dinner:

Snack:

Post-training protein:

6.00

7.00

8.00

9.00

10.00

11.00

12.00

13.00

14.00

15.00

16.00

17.00

18.00

19.00

■ Meditation   ■ 8 Glasses of Water

■ Stretching   ■ ....

Breakfast:

Snack:

Lunch:

Snack:

Dinner:

Snack:

Post-training protein:

6.00

7.00

8.00

9.00

10.00

11.00

12.00

13.00

14.00

15.00

16.00

17.00

18.00

19.00

Today I am excited to create...

Date

I am so grateful for these people in my life...

I create my day with my thoughts, therefore...

I AM

I AM

I AM

Workout:

Time/Duration:

Distance:

Intensity Level 1-10:

Reps/Weight:

Sequence:

Intervals:

What I Noticed:

Notes for Next Session:

Recovery Notes:

What did I love about today?

What would I like to let go of?

How can I make tomorrow better than today?

Date

Today I am going to really enjoy...

_____
_____
_____
_____
_____

■ Meditation   ▢ 8 Glasses of Water

■ Stretching   ■ ....

When I am grateful I open up to more...

Breakfast:

Snack:

Lunch:

Snack:

Dinner:

Snack:

Post-training protein:

Today...

I AM

I AM

I AM

Workout:

Time/Duration:

Distance:

Intensity Level 1-10:

Reps/Weight:

Sequence:

Intervals:

What I Noticed:

Notes for Next Session:

Recovery Notes:

What was interesting about today?

What habit would I like to develop after today?

What strengths did I use today?

6.00

7.00

8.00

9.00

10.00

11.00

12.00

13.00

14.00

15.00

16.00

17.00

18.00

19.00

Meditation   8 Glasses of Water

Stretching   ....

Date

Breakfast:

Snack:

Lunch:

Snack:

Dinner:

Snack:

Post-training protein:

Today, I give thanks for...

Today I honour how I feel and...

I AM

I AM

I AM

6.00	
7.00	
8.00	
9.00	
10.00	
11.00	
12.00	
13.00	
14.00	
15.00	
16.00	
17.00	
18.00	
19.00	

Workout:

Time/Duration:

Distance:

Intensity Level 1-10:

Reps/Weight:

Sequence:

Intervals:

What I Noticed:

Notes for Next Session:

Recovery Notes:

What was today's lesson?

What new behaviour can I adopt into my life?

What did I suceed at today?

Today I am open to the possibility of...

_____
_____
_____
_____
_____

Date

■ Meditation   ▢ 8 Glasses of Water

■ Stretching   ■

What I love about my body is...

I have a winning mindset and...

I AM

I AM

I AM

Workout:

Time/Duration:

Distance:

Intensity Level 1-10:

Reps/Weight:

Sequence:

Intervals:

What I Noticed:

Notes for Next Session:

Recovery Notes:

How was my mindset today?

What new habit do I want to adopt into my life?

How did I stay committed to my fitness goals today?

Breakfast:

Snack:

Lunch:

Snack:

Dinner:

Snack:

Post-training protein:

6.00

7.00

8.00

9.00

10.00

11.00

12.00

13.00

14.00

15.00

16.00

17.00

18.00

19.00

☐ Meditation   ☐ 8 Glasses of Water

☐ Stretching   ☐ ....

Breakfast:

Snack:

Lunch:

Snack:

Dinner:

Snack:

Post-training protein:

6:00

7:00

8:00

9:00

10:00

11:00

12:00

13:00

14:00

15:00

16:00

17:00

18:00

19:00

Today would be amazing if...

_____

_____

_____

_____

_____

Date

I am so grateful for the simple things like...

Today I am healthy and...

I AM

I AM

I AM

Workout:

Time/Duration:

Distance:

Intensity Level 1-10:

Reps/Weight:

Sequence:

Intervals:

What I Noticed:

Notes for Next Session:

Recovery Notes:

What was fantastic about today?

How can I drink more water during my days?

What negative attitude do I wish to let go of?

8 Week Check-In

Welcome to your 8-Week Check-in! It's time to celebrate your progress, identify what needs attention, record your progress with a photo and reset your focus for the next 4 weeks. Use your answers to the following questions to plan your next month and adjust your goals and training plan accordingly.

What major health goals have I achieved this month?

How can I be more congruent with my thoughts, words and actions?

What are the biggest distractions to my training and how can I remove them?

What is one thing I can do this week that will create the biggest results in my life?

What am I committed to achieving in my life right now?

How can I inspire myself and be inspirational to those around me?

What disempowering thoughts are holding me back and how can I upgrade those?

What fun new exercises can I incorporate into my current training sessions?

Record Your Progress With A Photo   Check 12 Week Goal Planner   Plan Training & Meals For This Wee

Review Body Blueprint   Review Purpose and Fitness Statement   Celebrate Your Progress!

10 Steps to a Positive Body Image

1. Appreciate all that your body can do for you.

2. Keep a top 10 list of what you like about yourself (not related to your body).

3. Remind yourself that true beauty is only skin deep. Beauty is a state of mind not a state of your body.

4. See yourself as a whole person, not just specific body parts.

5. Surround yourself with positive people who make you feel good about yourself.

6. Shut down those little voices in your head that tell you your body is not right or that you are a bad person.

7. Wear clothes that are comfortable and that make you feel good about your body.

8. Become a critical viewer of social and media messages.

9. Do something kind for yourself - something that lets your body know you appreciate it.

10. Use the time and energy that you usually spend worrying about food, calories and your weight and do something kind for yourself or to help others.

There are 1,440 minutes in a day, use 60 of them to exercise.

12 Week Goal Planner

Weeks 1 - 4

Fitness Goal:

Target date:
How I'm going to achieve this goal:
1.
2.
3.
4.
Why I'd love to achieve this goal:

How will I feel when I've reached this goal?

Fitness Goal:

Target date:
How I'm going to achieve this goal:
1.
2.
3.
4.
Why I'd love to achieve this goal:

How will I feel when I've reached this goal?

Fitness Goal:

Target date:
How I'm going to achieve this goal:
1.
2.
3.
4.
Why I'd love to achieve this goal:

How will I feel when I've reached this goal?

Weeks 5 - 8

Fitness Goal:

Target date:
How I'm going to achieve this goal:
1.
2.
3.
4.
Why I'd love to achieve this goal:

How will I feel when I've reached this goal?

Fitness Goal:

Target date:
How I'm going to achieve this goal:
1.
2.
3.
4.
Why I'd love to achieve this goal:

How will I feel when I've reached this goal?

Fitness Goal:

Target date:
How I'm going to achieve this goal:
1.
2.
3.
4.
Why I'd love to achieve this goal:

How will I feel when I've reached this goal?

Weeks 9 - 12

Fitness Goal:

Target date:
How I'm going to achieve this goal:
1.
2.
3.
4.
Why I'd love to achieve this goal:

How will I feel when I've reached this goal?

Fitness Goal:

Target date:
How I'm going to achieve this goal:
1.
2.
3.
4.
Why I'd love to achieve this goal:

How will I feel when I've reached this goal?

Fitness Goal:

Target date:
How I'm going to achieve this goal:
1.
2.
3.
4.
Why I'd love to achieve this goal:

How will I feel when I've reached this goal?

Weekly Planner

4 Major Goals I'm Focused On This Week:

1	2	3	4

Projects & Appointments For This Week	Time	Training, Stretching & Meals	Time
monday			
tuesday			
wednesday			
thursday			
friday			
saturday			
sunday			

Date

Today I would love...

_____

_____

_____

_____

| ■ Meditation | ■ 8 Glasses of Water |
| ■ Stretching | ■ .... |

Today I am so grateful for...

My intentions for today are...

I AM

I AM

I AM

Workout:

Time/Duration:

Distance:

Intensity Level 1-10:

Reps/Weight:

Sequence:

Intervals:

What I Noticed:

Notes for Next Session:

Recovery Notes:

What did I learn today?

After today, what behaviour do I want to upgrade?

What strengths did I use today?

Breakfast:

Snack:

Lunch:

Snack:

Dinner:

Snack:

Post-training protein:

6.00

7.00

8.00

9.00

10.00

11.00

12.00

13.00

14.00

15.00

16.00

17.00

18.00

19.00

Meditation ☐ 8 Glasses of Water

Stretching ☐ ....

Date

Breakfast:

Snack:

Lunch:

Snack:

Dinner:

Snack:

Post-training protein:

Today I'm going to appreciate...

The mindset I wish to create today is...

I AM

I AM

I AM

Workout:

Time/Duration:

Distance:

Intensity Level 1-10:

Reps/Weight:

Sequence:

Intervals:

What I Noticed:

Notes for Next Session:

Recovery Notes:

What did I enjoy about today?

What challenged me today that I can grow from?

What did I do really well today?

6.00

7.00

8.00

9.00

10.00

11.00

12.00

13.00

14.00

15.00

16.00

17.00

18.00

19.00

Today is going to be great because....

_____

_____

_____

_____

_____

Date

5 things I'm grateful for in my life are...

Today I am focusing on being...

I AM

I AM

I AM

Workout:

Time/Duration:

Distance:

Intensity Level 1-10:

Reps/Weight:

Sequence:

Intervals:

What I Noticed:

Notes for Next Session:

Recovery Notes:

What went well today?

What could I have handled differently today?

How healthy was my diet today?

Meditation   8 Glasses of Water

Stretching   ....

Breakfast:

Snack:

Lunch:

Snack:

Dinner:

Snack:

Post-training protein:

6.00

7.00

8.00

9.00

10.00

11.00

12.00

13.00

14.00

15.00

16.00

17.00

18.00

19.00

_____
_____
_____
_____
_____

Date

Meditation ☐   8 Glasses of Water ☐

Stretching ☐   ☐ ....

Breakfast:

Snack:

Lunch:

Snack:

Dinner:

Snack:

Post-training protein:

I am so grateful for these people in my life...

I create my day with my thoughts, therefore...

I AM

I AM

I AM

6.00

7.00

8.00

9.00

10.00

11.00

12.00

13.00

14.00

15.00

16.00

17.00

18.00

19.00

Workout:

Time/Duration:

Distance:

Intensity Level 1-10:

Reps/Weight:

Sequence:

Intervals:

What I Noticed:

Notes for Next Session:

Recovery Notes:

What did I love about today?

What would I like to let go of?

How can I make tomorrow better than today?

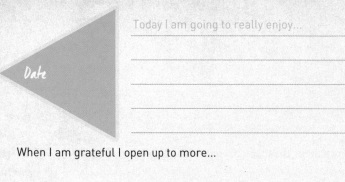

Date

Today I am going to really enjoy...

_____

_____

_____

_____

When I am grateful I open up to more...

	Meditation		8 Glasses of Water
	Stretching		....

Breakfast:

Snack:

Lunch:

Snack:

Dinner:

Snack:

Post-training protein:

Today...

I AM

I AM

I AM

Workout:

Time/Duration:

Distance:

Intensity Level 1-10:

Reps/Weight:

Sequence:

Intervals:

What I Noticed:

Notes for Next Session:

Recovery Notes:

What was interesting about today?

What habit would I like to develop after today?

What strengths did I use today?

6.00

7.00

8.00

9.00

10.00

11.00

12.00

13.00

14.00

15.00

16.00

17.00

18.00

19.00

☐ Meditation   ☐ 8 Glasses of Water

☐ Stretching   ☐ ....

Date

Breakfast:

Snack:

Lunch:

Snack:

Dinner:

Snack:

Post-training protein:

Today, I give thanks for...

Today I honour how I feel and...

I AM

I AM

I AM

6.00

7.00

8.00

9.00

10.00

11.00

12.00

13.00

Workout:

Time/Duration:

Distance:

Intensity Level 1-10:

Reps/Weight:

Sequence:

Intervals:

What I Noticed:

Notes for Next Session:

Recovery Notes:

What was today's lesson?

14.00

15.00

What new behaviour can I adopt into my life?

16.00

17.00

What did I suceed at today?

18.00

19.00

Weekly Check-in

09.00	12.00	15.00
10.00	13.00	16.00
11.00	14.00	17.00

What have I achieved on my 12 Week Body Blueprint this week?

■ Rocking Body: One Massive Action

■ Review 12 Week Goal Planner

What do I need to start or stop?

■ My Ideal Body Inspiration

■ Plan Training & Meals For This Week

How is my inner dialogue? How can I speak kinder to myself?

Old Habit >

What is one thing I can do this week that will create
the biggest results in my life?

New Habit >

Where is my current attitude on a scale from 1-10?
How can I get some more altitude and upgrade my attitude?

How can I be happier and healthier?

New Actions >

What negative attitudes are holding me back and how can I overcome those?

New Affirmation / Mantra

How can I stretch myself further in my training sessions?

4 Major Goals I'm Focused On This Week:

| 1 | 2 | 3 | 4 |

Projects & Appointments For This Week	Time	Training, Stretching & Meals	Time
monday			
tuesday			
wednesday			
thursday			
friday			
saturday			
sunday			

Good habits
are just as
addictive as
bad habits,
but much more
rewarding.

Today I am open to the possibility of...

_____
_____
_____
_____
_____

Date

Meditation   8 Glasses of Water

Stretching   ....

What I love about my body is...

I have a winning mindset and...

I AM

I AM

I AM

Breakfast:

Snack:

Lunch:

Snack: .

Dinner:

Snack:

Post-training protein:

Workout:

Time/Duration:

Distance:

Intensity Level 1-10:

Reps/Weight:

Sequence:

Intervals:

What I Noticed:

Notes for Next Session:

Recovery Notes:

How was my mindset today?

What new habit do I want to adopt into my life?

How did I stay committed to my fitness goals today?

6.00

7.00

8.00

9.00

10.00

11.00

12.00

13.00

14.00

15.00

16.00

17.00

18.00

19.00

□ Meditation □ 8 Glasses of Water

□ Stretching □ ....

Breakfast:

Snack:

Lunch:

Snack:

Dinner:

Snack:

Post-training protein:

6.00

7.00

8.00

9.00

10.00

11.00

12.00

13.00

14.00

15.00

16.00

17.00

18.00

19.00

Today would be amazing if...

_____

_____

_____

_____

_____

Date

I am so grateful for the simple things like...

Today I am healthy and...

I AM

I AM

I AM

Workout:

Time/Duration:

Distance:

Intensity Level 1-10:

Reps/Weight:

Sequence:

Intervals:

What I Noticed:

Notes for Next Session:

Recovery Notes:

What was fantastic about today?

How can I drink more water during my days?

What negative attitude do I wish to let go of?

Today I would love...

_____

_____

_____

_____

_____

Date

Meditation		8 Glasses of Water
Stretching		....

Today I am so grateful for...

My intentions for today are...

I AM

I AM

I AM

Workout:

Time/Duration:

Distance:

Intensity Level 1-10:

Reps/Weight:

Sequence:

Intervals:

What I Noticed:

Notes for Next Session:

Recovery Notes:

What did I learn today?

After today, what behaviour do I want to upgrade?

What strengths did I use today?

Breakfast:

Snack:

Lunch:

Snack:

Dinner:

Snack:

Post-training protein:

6.00

7.00

8.00

9.00

10.00

11.00

12.00

13.00

14.00

15.00

16.00

17.00

18.00

19.00

Date

- Meditation   - 8 Glasses of Water
- Stretching   - ....

Breakfast:

Snack:

Lunch:

Snack:

Dinner:

Snack:

Post-training protein:

Today I'm going to appreciate...

The mindset I wish to create today is...

I AM

I AM

I AM

6.00

7.00

8.00

9.00

10.00

11.00

12.00

13.00

14.00

15.00

16.00

17.00

18.00

19.00

Workout:

Time/Duration:

Distance:

Intensity Level 1-10:

Reps/Weight:

Sequence:

Intervals:

What I Noticed:

Notes for Next Session:

Recovery Notes:

What did I enjoy about today?

What challenged me today that I can grow from?

What did I do really well today?

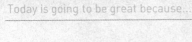

Today is going to be great because....

_____
_____
_____
_____
_____

Date

| ■ Meditation | ■ 8 Glasses of Water |
| ■ Stretching | ■ .... |

Breakfast:

Snack:

Lunch:

Snack:

Dinner:

Snack:

Post-training protein:

5 things I'm grateful for in my life are...

Today I am focusing on being...

I AM

I AM

I AM

Workout:

Time/Duration:

Distance:

Intensity Level 1-10:

Reps/Weight:

Sequence:

Intervals:

What I Noticed:

Notes for Next Session:

Recovery Notes:

What went well today?

What could I have handled differently today?

How healthy was my diet today?

6.00

7.00

8.00

9.00

10.00

11.00

12.00

13.00

14.00

15.00

16.00

17.00

18.00

19.00

Meditation 8 Glasses of Water

Stretching ....

Breakfast:

Snack:

Lunch:

Snack:

Dinner:

Snack:

Post-training protein:

6.00

7.00

8.00

9.00

10.00

11.00

12.00

13.00

14.00

15.00

16.00

17.00

18.00

19.00

Today I am excited to create...

_____

_____

_____

_____

_____

Date

I am so grateful for these people in my life...

I create my day with my thoughts, therefore...

I AM

I AM

I AM

Workout:

Time/Duration:

Distance:

Intensity Level 1-10:

Reps/Weight:

Sequence:

Intervals:

What I Noticed:

Notes for Next Session:

Recovery Notes:

What did I love about today?

What would I like to let go of?

How can I make tomorrow better than today?

Weekly Check-in

	09.00	12.00	15.00
	10.00	13.00	16.00
	11.00	14.00	17.00

What have I achieved this week?

What's working and why is it working?

What's not working and what am I willing to do to upgrade it?

What is one thing I can do this week that will create the biggest results towards my fitness goals?

Where is my current attitude on a scale from 1-10? How can I get some more altitude and upgrade my attitude?

Am I being self-honest about my diet and training?

What beliefs are holding me back and how can I upgrade those?

How can I make my training sessions more fun next week?

Rocking Body: One Massive Action

Review 12 Week Goal Planner

My Ideal Body Inspiration

Plan Training & Meals For This Week

Old Habit >

New Habit >

New Actions >

New Affirmation / Mantra

4 Major Goals I'm Focused On This Week:

1	2	3	4

Projects & Appointments For This Week	Time	Training, Stretching & Meals	Time
monday			
tuesday			
wednesday			
thursday			
friday			
saturday			
sunday			

1

The more muscles you have, the more calories you burn, even at rest.

Date

Today I am going to really enjoy...
_____
_____
_____
_____

■ Meditation   ■ 8 Glasses of Water
■ Stretching   ■ ....

When I am grateful I open up to more...

Breakfast:
Snack:
Lunch:
Snack:
Dinner:
Snack:
Post-training protein:

Today...

I AM
I AM
I AM

6.00

Workout:

Time/Duration:

7.00

Distance:

8.00

Intensity Level 1-10:

Reps/Weight:

9.00

Sequence:

10.00

Intervals:

What I Noticed:

11.00

Notes for Next Session:

12.00

Recovery Notes:

13.00

What was interesting about today?

14.00

15.00

What habit would I like to develop after today?

16.00

17.00

What strengths did I use today?

18.00

19.00

Meditation   8 Glasses of Water

Stretching   ....

Breakfast:

Snack:

Lunch:

Snack:

Dinner:

Snack:

Post-training protein:

6.00

7.00

8.00

9.00

10.00

11.00

12.00

13.00

14.00

15.00

16.00

17.00

18.00

19.00

Date

Today, I give thanks for...

Today I honour how I feel and...

I AM

I AM

I AM

Workout:

Time/Duration:

Distance:

Intensity Level 1-10:

Reps/Weight:

Sequence:

Intervals:

What I Noticed:

Notes for Next Session:

Recovery Notes:

What was today's lesson?

What new behaviour can I adopt into my life?

What did I suceed at today?

Date

Today I am open to the possibility of...

_____
_____
_____
_____
_____

Meditation   8 Glasses of Water

Stretching   ....

Breakfast:

Snack:

Lunch:

Snack:

Dinner:

Snack:

Post-training protein:

What I love about my body is...

I have a winning mindset and...

I AM

I AM

I AM

Workout:

Time/Duration:

Distance:

Intensity Level 1-10:

Reps/Weight:

Sequence:

Intervals:

What I Noticed:

Notes for Next Session:

Recovery Notes:

How was my mindset today?

What new habit do I want to adopt into my life?

How did I stay committed to my fitness goals today?

6.00

7.00

8.00

9.00

10.00

11.00

12.00

13.00

14.00

15.00

16.00

17.00

18.00

19.00

◼ Meditation ◼ 8 Glasses of Water

◼ Stretching ◼ ....

Breakfast:

Snack:

Lunch:

Snack:

Dinner:

Snack:

Post-training protein:

6.00

7.00

8.00

9.00

10.00

11.00

12.00

13.00

14.00

15.00

16.00

17.00

18.00

19.00

Today would be amazing if...

_____

_____

_____

_____

_____

I am so grateful for the simple things like...

Today I am healthy and...

I AM

I AM

I AM

Workout:

Time/Duration:

Distance:

Intensity Level 1-10:

Reps/Weight:

Sequence:

Intervals:

What I Noticed:

Notes for Next Session:

Recovery Notes:

What was fantastic about today?

How can I drink more water during my days?

What negative attitude do I wish to let go of?

Date

Date

Today I would love...

_____
_____
_____
_____

Meditation ☐   8 Glasses of Water ☐

Stretching ☐   ☐ ....

Breakfast:

Snack:

Lunch:

Snack:

Dinner:

Snack:

Post-training protein:

Today I am so grateful for...

My intentions for today are...

I AM

I AM

I AM

Workout:

Time/Duration:

Distance:

Intensity Level 1-10:

Reps/Weight:

Sequence:

Intervals:

What I Noticed:

Notes for Next Session:

Recovery Notes:

What did I learn today?

After today, what behaviour do I want to upgrade?

What strengths did I use today?

6.00

7.00

8.00

9.00

10.00

11.00

12.00

13.00

14.00

15.00

16.00

17.00

18.00

19.00

☐ Meditation ☐ 8 Glasses of Water

☐ Stretching ☐ ....

Breakfast:

Snack:

Lunch:

Snack:

Dinner:

Snack:

Post-training protein:

6.00

7.00

8.00

9.00

10.00

11.00

12.00

13.00

14.00

15.00

16.00

17.00

18.00

19.00

What if (insert possibility)...

Date

Today I'm going to appreciate...

The mindset I wish to create today is...

I AM

I AM

I AM

Workout:

Time/Duration:

Distance:

Intensity Level 1-10:

Reps/Weight:

Sequence:

Intervals:

What I Noticed:

Notes for Next Session:

Recovery Notes:

What did I enjoy about today?

What challenged me today that I can grow from?

What did I do really well today?

Weekly Check-in

09.00	12.00	15.00
10.00	13.00	16.00
11.00	14.00	17.00

What fitness goals have I completed this week?

What's going well and why is it?

What do I find most challenging about my fitness goals so far?

What is one thing I can do this week that will create
the biggest results in my life?

Where is my current attitude on a scale from 1-10?
How can I get some more altitude and upgrade my attitude?

How can I be more empowered in my thoughts, words and actions?

What fears are holding me back and how can I overcome those?

How does my body feel this week?

■ Rocking Body: One Massive Action

■ Review 12 Week Goal Planner

■ My Ideal Body Inspiration

■ Plan Training & Meals For This Week

Old Habit >

New Habit >

New Actions >

New Affirmation / Mantra

Weekly Planner

4 Major Goals I'm Focused On This Week:

1	2	3	4

Projects & Appointments For This Week	Time	Training, Stretching & Meals	Time
monday			
tuesday			
wednesday			
thursday			
friday			
saturday			
sunday			

Begin to think
of yourself
as becoming
the person you
want to be.

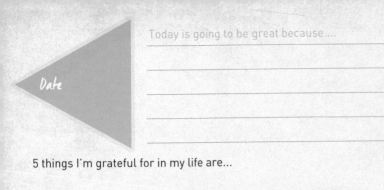

Today is going to be great because....
_____
_____
_____
_____
_____

Date

Meditation   8 Glasses of Water

Stretching   ....

Breakfast:

Snack:

Lunch:

Snack:

Dinner:

Snack:

Post-training protein:

5 things I'm grateful for in my life are...

Today I am focusing on being...

I AM

I AM

I AM

Workout:

Time/Duration:

Distance:

Intensity Level 1-10:

Reps/Weight:

Sequence:

Intervals:

What I Noticed:

Notes for Next Session:

Recovery Notes:

What went well today?

What could I have handled differently today?

How healthy was my diet today?

6.00

7.00

8.00

9.00

10.00

11.00

12.00

13.00

14.00

15.00

16.00

17.00

18.00

19.00

Meditation   8 Glasses of Water

Stretching   ....

Date

Breakfast:

Snack:

Lunch:

Snack:

Dinner:

Snack:

Post-training protein:

I am so grateful for these people in my life...

I create my day with my thoughts, therefore...

I AM

I AM

I AM

6.00

7.00

Workout:

8.00

Time/Duration:

Distance:

9.00

Intensity Level 1-10:

Reps/Weight:

10.00

Sequence:

11.00

Intervals:

What I Noticed:

12.00

Notes for Next Session:

Recovery Notes:

13.00

What did I love about today?

14.00

15.00

What would I like to let go of?

16.00

17.00

How can I make tomorrow better than today?

18.00

19.00

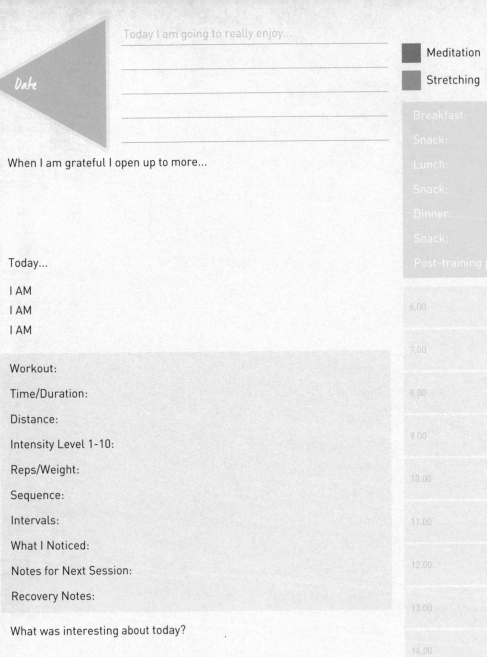

Today I am going to really enjoy...
_____
_____
_____
_____

Date

■ Meditation   ▢ 8 Glasses of Water
■ Stretching   ■ ....

When I am grateful I open up to more...

Breakfast:

Snack:

Lunch:

Snack:

Dinner:

Snack:

Post-training protein:

Today...

I AM

I AM

I AM

Workout:

Time/Duration:

Distance:

Intensity Level 1-10:

Reps/Weight:

Sequence:

Intervals:

What I Noticed:

Notes for Next Session:

Recovery Notes:

What was interesting about today?

What habit would I like to develop after today?

What strengths did I use today?

6.00

7.00

8.00

9.00

10.00

11.00

12.00

13.00

14.00

15.00

16.00

17.00

18.00

19.00

□ Meditation   □ 8 Glasses of Water

□ Stretching   □ ....

Breakfast:

Snack:

Lunch:

Snack:

Dinner:

Snack:

Post-training protein:

	6.00
	7.00
	8.00
	9.00
	10.00
	11.00
	12.00
	13.00
	14.00
	15.00
	16.00
	17.00
	18.00
	19.00

Today is my opportunity to...

Date

Today, I give thanks for...

Today I honour how I feel and...

I AM
I AM
I AM

Workout:

Time/Duration:

Distance:

Intensity Level 1-10:

Reps/Weight:

Sequence:

Intervals:

What I Noticed:

Notes for Next Session:

Recovery Notes:

What was today's lesson?

What new behaviour can I adopt into my life?

What did I suceed at today?

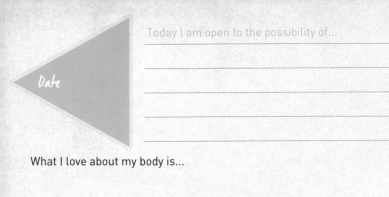

Today I am open to the possibility of...

Date

What I love about my body is...

I have a winning mindset and...

I AM
I AM
I AM

Workout:

Time/Duration:

Distance:

Intensity Level 1-10:

Reps/Weight:

Sequence:

Intervals:

What I Noticed:

Notes for Next Session:

Recovery Notes:

How was my mindset today?

What new habit do I want to adopt into my life?

How did I stay committed to my fitness goals today?

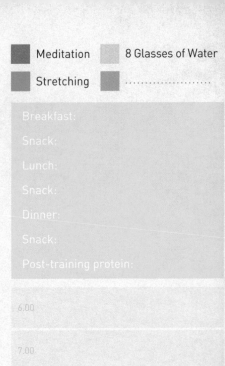

Meditation   8 Glasses of Water

Stretching   ....

Breakfast:

Snack:

Lunch:

Snack:

Dinner:

Snack:

Post-training protein:

6.00

7.00

8.00

9.00

10.00

11.00

12.00

13.00

14.00

15.00

16.00

17.00

18.00

19.00

_____
_____
_____
_____

Date

■ Meditation   ■ 8 Glasses of Water

■ Stretching   ■ ....

Breakfast:

Snack:

Lunch:

Snack:

Dinner:

Snack:

Post-training protein:

I am so grateful for the simple things like...

Today I am healthy and...

I AM

I AM

I AM

6.00

7.00

8.00

9.00

10.00

11.00

12.00

13.00

14.00

15.00

16.00

17.00

18.00

19.00

Workout:

Time/Duration:

Distance:

Intensity Level 1-10:

Reps/Weight:

Sequence:

Intervals:

What I Noticed:

Notes for Next Session:

Recovery Notes:

What was fantastic about today?

How can I drink more water during my days?

What negative attitude do I wish to let go of?

12 Week Rocking Body Review

If you've made it to this point in the journal, it's likely you've gone through an incredible body, mind, spirit transformation. Congratulations on your amazing commitment, effort and determination! Now it's time to reflect back over the last 12 weeks and note your achievements, your challenges and your breakthroughs, and to celebrate how far you've come. Use your observations as stepping-stones to catapult you into another 12 week transformation.

Now that you've completed the Dailygreatness Training Journal, join Rocking Fit, our 12 week online holistic training program for women at **www.rockingfit.com** and get ready to be energised, empowered and inspired even more!

Plus, use discount code **RFDGTJ** to receive 15% off your membership.

Share your journal images using hashtag **#rockingfit** on social media or review the Dailygreatness Training Journal on Amazon and go in our monthly draw to win a free copy.

To reorder your Dailygreatness Training Journal and browse all our other journals, online courses and content, visit www.dailygreatness.co

- [ ] Review your Rocking Body Blueprint
- [ ] Review your Purpose Statement
- [ ] Review your 12 Week Goal Planner
- [ ] Reset your goals and focus for another 12 Week Challenge!

My New Rocking Fit Body

Your photo

My Weight

My Measurements

What major fitness goals have I achieved this past 12 weeks?

How much closer am I to my ideal rocking fit body?

What new empowered habits have I adopted?

How am I embracing my new healthy lifestyle?

What breakthroughs have I had?

How has my overall attitude changed since using the Dailygreatness Training Journal?

What challenges have I faced and overcome?

How is my energy level and general enthusiasm for life?

What have I learned about myself?

How have my relationships improved since I started training?

What new fitness goals would I like to focus on for the next 12 weeks?

Appendix i

Basic Meditation Technique

Sit in a comfortable position. You may like to sit on a chair, or cross-legged on the floor (you can sit on a blanket, towel or book if that helps your knees and hips relax a little more). You want to be able to completely relax while staying fully alert. Close your eyes and begin to focus on your breath.

As you inhale and exhale, focus on the rise and fall of your belly or the breath at the tip of your nose. Begin to clear you mind with each new breath. The idea is to stay unattached to your thoughts, and as they arise, (which they will) just let them go without continuing to worry about or attach to them. Think of your thoughts as clouds and as they float into your mind, just let them drift right on by and keep letting go.

Focus instead on your breath, and soon the quiet space in between your thoughts will increase. As you practice this technique, you will naturally progress to being able to meditate for longer periods, but begin with just 10 to 15 minutes, and over time aim to progress to 25-40 minutes.

References

www.beachbody.com
www.rockingfit.com
www.nationaleatingdisorders.org

About the Author

Lyndelle Palmer-Clarke began her career in the entertainment industry as a singer, songwriter, actress and tv presenter. At 18, she was touring her band as the lead singer and manager around her home country of Australia. At 21 she signed to a major record label and travelled the world writing and recording with some of the worlds' biggest writers and producers and in 2006 was a finalist on Australian Idol. After moving to London to further pursue her music career, her life began to unravel with a series of crises that led to severe depression and hitting rock bottom. After much soul searching and re-evaluating her future in the entertainment industry, Lyndelle realised that her goals had become unhealthy and were, in fact, holding her back from evolving into the person she wanted to become. This realisation was the catalyst for leaving the entertainment industry and pursuing her passion for personal development. As a student of personal growth and spirituality for more than a decade, Lyndelle was disillusioned with the self-improvement industry as her life was clearly not reflecting all the knowledge she'd garnered from the self-help books, seminars and gurus she'd followed. Realising that the crucial missing piece was applied knowledge, she set out to create a series of practical journals to help people apply what they already knew into their daily lives in a dynamic way. Transitioning into a career as an author, publisher and mentor, she now writes, speaks and shares her message of personal transformation, wellness, creativity, entrepreneurship and becoming more conscious in everyday life. It has become her mission to help others raise their consciousness, to live more powerful, purposeful lives, and to not only survive but to pursue their dreams and thrive. Follow Lyndelle at **www.lyndellepalmerclarke.com**